C000027377

COLLINS
COBUILD

KEY WORDS IN
SCIENCE &
TECHNOLOGY

COLLINS COBUILD

KEY WORDS IN SCIENCE & TECHNOLOGY

Bill Mascull

THE UNIVERSITY
OF BIRMINGHAM

COLLINS
COBUILD

HarperCollins*Publishers*

HarperCollins Publishers
77-85 Fulham Palace Road
London   W6 8JB

COBUILD is a trademark of William Collins Sons & Co Ltd

© HarperCollins Publishers 1997

First published 1997

2 4 6 8 1 0 9 7 5 3 1

ISBN 0 00 375098 1

Design and typesetting by
eMC Design, Bromham, Bedfordshire

Printed and bound in Great Britain by
Scotprint Ltd, Musselburgh.

The COBUILD Series

Founding Editor-in-Chief	John Sinclair
Editorial Director	Gwyneth Fox
Editor	Michael Lax
Administration	Michelle Devereux

We would also like to thank Stephen Lax
for his helpful comments on the text.

Corpus Acknowledgements

We would like to acknowledge the assistance of the many hundreds of individuals
and companies who have kindly given permission for copyright material to be
used in The Bank of English. The written sources include many national and
regional newspapers in Britain and overseas; magazine and periodical publishers;
and book publishers in Britain, the United States, and Australia. Extensive spoken
data has been provided by radio and television broadcasting companies; research
workers at many universities and other institutions; and numerous individual
contributors. We are grateful to them all.

Note

http://www.cobuild.collins.co.uk

Contents

Introduction

Key Words in Science and Technology is designed to help you understand and use the essential vocabulary of science and technology in English.

It systematically covers words and expressions that frequently occur and recur in popular science reporting. Some of these occur almost exclusively in scientific contexts; others are used in general English but are used in a particular way when talking about science.

This book shows what these words and expressions mean, how they are used, and how they relate to each other.

Key Words in Science and Technology covers six main subject areas. There is also an introductory chapter on the language of research, discovery, and innovation in general. You look at the meanings of frequently occurring words in these areas in the context of real examples taken from newspapers and magazines.

You then go on to apply and develop your knowledge of meaning and usage in specially devised language activities, many of them based on longer extracts and articles. These have been chosen for their topicality and relevance to everyone interested in science and technology.

Key Words in Science and Technology has been written so that each chapter can be read sequentially from beginning to end. Or you may just want to dip and browse, looking at things,that interest you. A special cross-reference system helps you to do this.

Structure

Each chapter consists of a logical sequence of topic sections. Each topic section contains these parts:

◆ **Key words and commentary.** The key words in a specific area are listed, explained and defined in relation to each other and in their grammatical context.

◆ **Examples** illustrate the meanings of these key words in context. Most of the extracts are at least one sentence or longer so as to give a good sense of overall context. The examples have been chosen not only for their interest, but also for their illustrative and explanatory power.

◆ **Language activities** further refine understanding of how the key words are used, relate to each other and to other words; develop awareness of grammatical context; and show how the key words fit into overall patterns of meaning. Many of the activities are based on long extracts which can be used for group discussion.

Section content

Key words, commentary, and language notes

Each commentary brings together a number of related key words under a section heading, explaining and defining them in a continuous text. The key words are indicated in **bold** in the commentary itself and are also listed in logical groups in the shaded box.

Frequent collocations (word combinations) are also indicated.

Where relevant, the commentary is followed by language notes providing grammatical information about key words in the commentary (where this information is not given in the commentary itself) and giving variations in spelling and hyphenation.

Micro-organisms 1

micro-organism

microbiologist
microbiology

bacteria
bacteriologist
bacteriology

virologist
virology
virus

The study of **micro-organisms**, very small living things, is **microbiology**, undertaken by **microbiologists**.

The study of **bacteria**, single-cell organisms without a nucleus, is **bacteriology** and specialists in this area are **bacteriologists**.

nucleus *140* ⇓

Viruses are extremely small organisms invisible even under a microscope. Studying them is **virology** and its specialists are **virologists**.

virus *68* ⇑

◆ **LANGUAGE NOTE**
Micro-organism is also spelled as one word.
The singular form of **bacteria** is **bacterium**.

Examples

The examples have been chosen to provide interesting illustrations of how the key words are used. They are in italics, and the first occurrence of a key word is underlined.

The new experiments are an attempt to explain high levels of ozone in the troposphere across much of the southern hemisphere during parts of the year. This phenomenon was revealed in 1990 by <u>data</u> collected by NASA satellites.

Cross-referencing

An arrow with a page number in the right-hand margin indicates that a word in the text is defined as a key word in another chapter of the book. Key words dealt with elsewhere in the same chapter and very common words such as 'scientist' and 'experiment' are not indicated in this way.

Most of these academies of science had no ecologists in them and didn't regard ecology as a <u>science</u>.

ecologist *31* ⇓
ecology *31* ⇓

Likewise if a key word is defined in two places, either with the same meaning or a different meaning, arrows point to the other occurrence.

nuclear energy
nuclear power
nuclear weapons

Fission is the source of energy used to generate electricity: **nuclear energy** or **nuclear power**; and of bombs and other arms: **nuclear weapons**.

nuclear energy *40* ⇑
nuclear power *40* ⇑

The cross-reference system is designed to encourage you to browse, following your own routes through the book.

There is also a full index at the back of the book.

Language activities, and hints on how to do them

Each activity gets you to do one of these things, or a combination of them:

◆ Find a word missing from a number of different contexts by looking at meaning and grammar.

◆ Think about words and their meanings by putting them into an overall context. Where a list of words is given for gap completion of sentences or a text, read the instructions carefully: some of the words may be used more than once.

◆ Match words to their definitions. Look through all the items before completing the exercise: don't jump to conclusions.

◆ Match sentences or sentence-parts to take meaning, context, and grammar into account. Look specially for clues to help you combine sentence-parts not only meaningfully but grammatically.

◆ Re-order sentences and paragraphs to build logically developed texts, sometimes sorting out extracts from different sources. Read the instructions carefully for clues on which part comes first. Again, look specially for clues to help you combine sections not only meaningfully but grammatically to build up logically developed texts.

◆ Read articles and texts and answer questions designed not only to test understanding of key words but also to develop this understanding in wider contexts. Look at networks of meaning, reusing the key vocabulary of the chapter, relating it to what you already know. You may need to look up some words in a dictionary, such as the *Collins Cobuild English Dictionary*.

◆ Test your knowledge of meaning and spelling of words in the crosswords which conclude each unit.

Conventions

Language activities

Where language activities require missing words to be given, a continuous line indicates that the word (or occasionally words) may be of any length, as here:

1 The entertainment industry and the military are already the most important developers of virtual reality _____ , but to prosper, the technology needs to be taken up by the business world.

Where spaces are indicated like this, each underlining indicates one missing letter:

contract
recover
recovery

ailing
ill
sick

diseased

If you _ _ _ _ _ _ _ _ a disease, you get it. If you _ _ _ _ _ _ _ from an illness, you get better again: you make a

_ _ _ _ _ _ _ _ .

Someone with an illness is _ _ _ , _ _ _ _ , or less frequently,

_ _ _ _ _ _ .

Parts of the body that are not functioning normally are _ _ _ _ _ _ _ _ . It is not usual to say that someone is diseased.

'Gift' letters may sometimes be given, like this:

The Art of the Soluble

...Science is, in Peter Medawar's words, the art of the soluble. A good scientist knows that the trick is to choose a problem that is ripe for solution, both because the technology is there and because the concepts are in place.

1 A problem that is ripe for solution is
r _ _ _ y to be s _ _ _ _ d .

Note on sources

Key Words in Science and Technology has been developed using text databases containing nearly 100 million words of text from a variety of newspaper and magazine sources.

The sources from The Bank of English include:

New Scientist. British scientific weekly. Circulation 120,000.

The Economist. British weekly. Focus not exclusively economic, but also political, cultural, and scientific. Circulation 500,000 – half in the United States.

The Times. Daily. Circulation 700,000.

Sunday Times. Sister paper to *The Times.* Circulation 1,200,000.

The *Independent.* Daily, founded in 1987. Circulation 300,000.

Independent on Sunday. Sister paper to the *Independent.* Circulation 300,000.

The Guardian. Left of centre daily. Circulation 400,000.

Other sources include *Nature.* British professional scientific weekly. Circulation 55,000.

Science and scientists

science

scientific

scientist

Science is the study of the nature and behaviour of natural things and the knowledge obtained about them. A **science** is a particular area of scientific knowledge and study, or the study of an area of human behaviour.

Scientific describes things that relate to science.

A **scientist** is someone who works in science.

BIG SCIENCE   LITTLE SCIENCE

Science is a force that should be used for the good of humanity.

Most of these academies of science had no ecologists in them and didn't regard ecology as a science.

The Centre is running a series of talks on the relationship between science and literature, in which writers, poets and scientists discuss how scientific ideas over the past two centuries have influenced literature and social change.

ecologist **31** ⇓
ecology **31** ⇓

1 Science partners. The words in the box can all come in front of 'science'. Find combinations that refer to:

1 science that is not concerned with practical or commercial applications (2 expressions)

2 science that is concerned with practical or commercial applications

3 science books and TV programmes meant for the general public

4 science that does not have serious theoretical backing

5 science that requires many resources and very large sums of money

6 what economics is sometimes known as: the _____ science

	big		
pseudo-		basic	
	science		
popular			applied
	dismal	pure	

Now use the expressions to complete these extracts. Each expression is used once.

a Asimov spoke out in favour of science and reason and against _____ science and superstition.

b Research and development largely takes place in industry, and although it involves some _____ science, it really consists of the application of science and the improvement of technology.

c Developing and marketing new drugs has little to do with _____ science and everything to do with power and money.   **drug 87 ⇓**

d *Black Holes and Time Warps* goes far beyond the average _____ science books by presenting the general reader with a detailed historical account of one area of physics research.

e In _____ science, the national pride that sets country against country and scientist against scientist can be costly. The great projects of understanding have now reached such a scale that they are best served by the united efforts of all the world.

f Some economists are trying to give their _____ science sex appeal.

g When the Gillette company started investigating the _____ science of shaving in the 1950s, it was reacting to the threat of a cream that would dissolve beards.

Types of science

| hard science |
| soft science |

There are those who consider that some sciences are more 'scientific' than others, and they distinguish between **hard sciences** like physics and chemistry and **soft sciences** like psychology and anthropology. The division may be drawn almost anywhere, as the second example indicates.

Scientists in the hard sciences should not be too content with themselves. How many different answers exist, for example, to the following questions: how old is the universe, is the universe expanding or contracting, how many fundamental particles exist, when is the next earthquake due, what causes AIDS or Alzheimer's disease?

universe **153** ⇓
particle **140** ⇓
disease **81** ⇓

The statistics brought out a gender division between hard and soft science: girls tending towards biology, boys towards maths and physics.

2 **Science quiz.** Match these sciences to their areas of study.

1	anthropology	a	environment
2	biology	b	human mind and behaviour
3	chemistry	c	language
4	ecology	d	living things
5	economics	e	matter and forces
6	linguistics	f	money, industry, and trade
7	mathematics	g	numbers, quantities, and shapes
8	meteorology	h	people, society, and culture
9	physics	i	substances and their reactions
10	psychology	j	weather

3 **Science divisions.** Look at the examples and complete the commentary below.

Economists have begun to study the implications of near-rationality. To do so, they are drawing on research in sociology, anthropology, and above all, psychology. Since economics is a behavioural science, this extension of its research programme is long overdue.

At university, I rediscovered that attraction in earth sciences, finding out how ordinary things, rocks, rivers and the wind, became the way they are.

He is fascinated by the car in its fundamental role. 'Ergonomics is really the application, the technological side, of the other human sciences,' he explains. 'We are constantly aware that the skill involved in driving a car is phenomenal, but taken for granted.'

There has been a huge increase in medical and biomedical science over the decade. In the US, for example, one-third of all scientists are now engaged in the life sciences.

medical **80** ⇓

…Newton's three laws of motion, which, it was thought, could theoretically explain (eventually) all the phenomena of the natural world. The influence of this work spread beyond the natural sciences to virtually all subjects.

3

Decisions taken in the 1950s led to the bulk of science funding going into medicine, <u>physical sciences</u> such as nuclear power, and space research.

medicine **80** ⇓
nuclear power **144** ⇓
space **153** ⇓

Wisdom argues that the <u>social sciences</u> should rub shoulders with the natural sciences on equal terms.

behavioural science
earth science
human science
life science
natural science
physical science
social science

The _____ **sciences** are those dealing with the naturally occurring world in general. They include _____ **sciences** such as physics and chemistry. _____ **sciences** include geology and oceanography. _____ **sciences** include areas such as medicine and biology.

Studies of human behaviour such as economics or sociology are _____ **sciences**, _____ **sciences**, or _____ **sciences**.

◆ **LANGUAGE NOTE**
   Behavioural is spelled **behavioral** in American English.

Technology and technologists

technology
technological
technologist

high-tech
high-technology
hi-tech

low-tech
low-technology

Technology describes scientific knowledge applied for practical purposes. A **technology** is scientific knowledge applied in a particular area. **Technological** describes things relating to technology. **Technologists** are researchers who work in a particular area of technology.

Some technologies are more complex than others. Products, systems or industries using advanced technologies are **high-technology**, **high-tech**, or **hi-tech**. Those at the other end of the scale are **low-technology** or **low-tech**, but not 'lo-tech'.

◆ **LANGUAGE NOTE**
   High-technology and **low-technology** are also spelled without hyphens, especially when used as nouns.

Technology has made the world much smaller.

Over $1 billion a year has gone on research into nuclear fusion, a <u>technology</u> that has not yet generated a joule of electricity.

nuclear fusion
146 ⇓

Why has the pace of <u>technological</u> change accelerated so rapidly in the 20th century? Science is always on the move. Its preference is to find a question that nobody knew needed answering, answer it and then move on, leaving <u>technologists</u> to turn the answer into a machine, a drug or a computer program.

drug **87** ⇓
computer program **63** ⇓

Pressure has increased for the European Space Agency to cut back its big, <u>high-technology</u> projects, such as the spaceplane Hermes and the space station module Columbus.

space **153** ⇓
space station **163** ⇓

Since the 1950s the Defense Advanced Research Projects Agency has laid the foundations of various <u>high-tech</u> industries, such as computing and satellite building.

computing 53 ⇓
satellite 157 ⇓

Gerald Harris says he does not like anything <u>hi-tech</u>, so he has kept everything in his home-made submarine nice and simple.

… training doctors and nurses to work in the villages, and concentrating resources on cheap but effective medicines and <u>low-technology</u> equipment.

medicine 80 ⇓

The best-selling mopeds are made by Tomos, a firm that is content to produce <u>low-tech</u>, but unbeatably cheap, machines.

leading edge state of the art	The most advanced products and systems are said to be at the **leading edge** of technology or to represent the **state of the art.**

◆ **LANGUAGE NOTE**
Leading edge and **state of the art** are also spelled with hyphens, especially when used as adjectives.

The <u>leading edge</u> of technology is the laser. Scientists regard the laser as the ideal form of communication.

The book gives a succinct account of the technology of virtual reality and its history, from the pioneering work done in the 1960s to current <u>state of the art</u>.

virtual reality 75 ⇓

4 Technology partners. The words in the box can all come in front of 'technology'. Find combinations that refer to technology:

1   that is more complex than others (2 expressions)

2   that is not up-to-date (2 expressions)

3   that is up-to-date

4   that is neither high nor low

5   collectively to mean the computer and telecommunications industries

6   used in computers and telecommunications

7   that is known to work

8   that has not been shown to work

9   that does not rely on wires and cables

10   that is used in making things industrially

outdated

advanced   intermediate

wireless   information

primitive   **technology**   proven

untried   modern

sophisticated   digital

manufacturing

Inventors

| invent |
| invention |
| inventor |
| inventive |
| inventiveness |

Invention or **inventiveness** is the ability to design new machines, devices, or products. An **invention** is a new machine, device, or product.

People who **invent** things are **inventors**. The associated adjective is **inventive**.

He worked for the Bell Telephone Laboratories, helping that renowned centre of invention to develop automatic tracking radar, television transmission systems and efficient coding devices.

The country with the most Nobel prizes per head - Britain - is notoriously slow at commercialising inventions. Japan, to this day, stands as living proof that brilliant technological inventiveness can exist in a country with a lacklustre tradition of basic science.

Even after the industrial revolution had applied science to technology, the successful <u>inventors</u>, the Edisons and Marconis, were little concerned with science.

Newcomen <u>invented</u> a steam engine by copying a piece of apparatus invented by Denis Papin, a French scientist.

People are so much more flexible and <u>inventive</u> than robots.

5 Inevitable inventions. Read this article from *The Economist* and answer the questions.

The Art of the Soluble

...Science is, in Peter Medawar's words, the art of the soluble. A good scientist knows that the trick is to choose a problem that is ripe for solution, both because the technology is there and because the concepts are in place.

This explains the abundance of examples of simultaneous discoveries in the history of science: Adams and Leverrier found Neptune at the same time and accused each other of plagiarism, contributing mightily to a mood of Anglo-French dislike. Newton and Leibnitz; Darwin and Wallace; Gallo and Montagnier: the list is long.

Scientists speak of the 'inevitability' of discoveries in sharp contrast to other historical events. The structure of DNA would not have remained mysterious for long if Francis Crick and James Watson had not existed. James Watt was not indispensable to progress, though the steam engine was. There is irony here.

Faraday's invention of the electric motor has done more to change your life today than Lee's defeat at the Battle of Gettysburg. But who can doubt that history would have taken a different course if Lee had won that battle, whereas somebody other than Faraday would have invented the electric motor. ...

1 A problem that is ripe for solution is
<u>r</u> _ _ _ <u>y</u> to be <u>s</u> _ _ _ _ <u>d</u> .

2 If there is an abundance of things, are there a lot of them?

3 If you plagiarize someone or something, you _ _ _ _ them.

4 Are inevitable events avoidable?

DNA 111 ⇓

5 Would progress have been made without Crick, Faraday, Watson, and Watt?

Innovators

innovate
innovation
innovator
innovative

Innovation is the act of thinking of new ideas, developments, and improvements. These are **innovations** and the people **innovating** them are **innovators**. The associated adjective is **innovative**.

...a compendium of inventors and <u>innovators</u> associated with the town. It seems that 'paper, banknotes, printing machines, tin cans, lifts, wire, aeroplanes and many medicines all owe their modern existence to people who lived or worked in Dartford.'   **medicine 80** ⇓

The first invention is but a fraction of <u>innovation</u>. One reason is obvious: the first invention is, by later standards, primitive. The first electronic digital computer contained 18,000 vacuum tubes and filled a room 100 feet long.

The Japanese appetite for foreign technology is one that supplements a fruitful home-grown crop. The Japanese <u>innovate</u> at home and actively collaborate in the <u>innovations</u> of others.

The idea of representing data with music rather than showing it on a computer screen is just one of many <u>innovative</u> ideas to help the 100,000 scientists and engineers around the world whose disabilities include blindness, deafness, impaired mobility and dyslexia.

experimental

prototype

The first, **experimental**, versions of a new technological idea are **prototypes**.

A group of German researchers has devised a way to cut dramatically the emissions of nitrogen oxides and sulphur dioxide from diesel engines. Their <u>experimental</u> system pumps an electric current through the exhaust gases to render the pollutants harmless.   **emissions 46** ⇓

pollutant 34 ⇓

The technology, known as Electronic Paper, has been developed by Thorn EMI's Central Research Laboratories. CRL has built a 13-centimetre screen to prove that the idea works, and promises a <u>prototype</u> version in six months.

6 **Blind invention.** Read this article from *The Economist* and answer the questions.

The Shock of the Not Quite New

It is a commonplace that technologies move only slowly from first invention to widespread use. What is striking in the history of technological innovation, however, is that the dispersion of a new technology is not just slow but extraordinarily uncertain even after its first commercial applications have been realised.

This runs against the conventional wisdom, which holds that the uncertainties are much reduced after the first commercial use. The evidence to refute that view comes not just from any old technologies, but from many of the most important innovations of this century.

Consider the laser, a comparatively young technology with more development in store. Beyond uses in measurement, navigation and chemical research, applications have expanded to include the reproduction of music (to make the laser a household product); surgery; printing; the cutting of cloth and other materials; and, its most significant use to date, telecommunications.

Together with fibre optics, the laser has revolutionised the telephone business, yet lawyers at Bell Labs were initially unwilling even to apply for a patent for their invention, believing it had no relevance to the telephone industry.

If that story sounds familiar, there is a reason: such a pattern of innovation is not exceptional, nor even quite common, but typical. The steam engine was invented in the eighteenth century as a way of pumping water out of mines; it remained nothing more than a pump for many years. Then it became a source of power for industry, then a source of power for transport, then a way to generate electricity. The first inventors never dreamed of such a breadth of application (or of electricity, for that matter). ...

1 If something is a commonplace, is it unusual?

2 If something disperses, it s p _ _ _ _ s .

3 Does 'realised' mean 'understood' in its context here?

4 Is the conventional wisdom a minority view?

5 If an opinion is refuted, is it disproved?

6 Has the laser reached the end of its development?

7 'Applications have expanded': they have g _ _ _ n .

surgery 97 ⇓

8 The most significant use of something is its most i _ _ _ _ _ _ _ t use.

9 Is 'apply' used here in the same way as 'application' in the previous paragraph?

10 If something follows a pattern, have similar events already happened?

11 These inventors never dreamed the applications would be so w i d e _ _ _ _ _ _ _ .

9

Technophiles and technophobes

technophile
technophobe

Someone who likes and understands technology is a
technophile; someone who does not, a **technophobe**.

For a technophile *nation like Australia, the Internet is a treasure.*   **Internet 72** ⇓

The fax machine is now found in millions of American homes. There are few technophobes *in modern
America.*

7 **Technophilia and technophobia.** Complete this article from the *New Scientist*
with the listed words. (b occurs three times, d twice and the others once each.)

a innovate   c innovating   e technophile
b innovation   d innovators   f technophobe

Innovators and Laggards

...My advice to anyone about to launch a new technology is to look
at how a new _____ (1) diffuses through the populace. ...

There seem to be five clear groups of individuals. The first are the
_____ (2). These are individuals who are always seeking to
_____ (3) or try out new ideas or equipment. They come in
many shapes or forms: the Clive Sinclair type of _____ (4)
genius; the adult who, deprived of a train set as a child has been
compensating ever since; the socially inadequate _____ (5)
who prefers electricity to interaction.

They had CDs, computers, microwaves and faxes long before most
people even knew what they were. Some may be _____ (6)
junkies who go for anything new and different, irrespective of quality, usefulness, or design. ...

Finally, come the 'laggards'. Like _____ (7), they come in different forms: the _____ (8), terrified of anything not simple
and mechanical; the young fogey who rejoices in the quill pen over
the computer; the ultra-cautious, who hate learning anything new.
They all share a fear and hostility towards _____ (9). ...

White coats

study

research
  research study

laboratory
  research laboratory
lab
  research lab

researcher

People trying to find facts about something **study** it or do **research** in it, into it, or on it.

A piece of research may be referred to as a **study** or a **research study**. These terms also refer to the published results of the research.

Scientific research often takes place in **laboratories**, or **labs**. These are also **research laboratories** or **research labs**.

People doing research are **researchers**.

◆ **LANGUAGE NOTE**
Research is a noun and a verb. As a noun, it is usually but not always an uncount noun.

Psychiatrists have spoken with respect of her <u>researches</u> into the possibility of detecting mental illness through handwriting.

Ciba-Geigy, the Swiss pharmaceuticals giant, has reduced from 18 to 7 the number of subjects which it <u>researches</u> in-house.

Many <u>studies</u> have shown that in the <u>laboratory</u> at least, amphibians such as frogs fail to develop normally at the acidity levels of some ponds.

Asking social science researchers to explain the four or five most important findings of a major <u>research study</u> is more likely to cause resentment than enthusiasm.

In this journal, Jim Horne, director of the sleep <u>research laboratory</u> at Loughborough University, described current thinking about dreams and sleep. He held that few <u>researchers</u> still believe that dreams 'have such sexual connotations as Freud believed'.

Sapienza's book 'Managing Scientists' offers a painless way to improve the psychological health of just about any <u>lab</u>.

At one event, BT's <u>research lab</u> at Martlesham showed off its leading-edge ideas.

boffin
men in white coats
people in white coats

Journalists often refer to scientific researchers as **boffins**, **men in white coats**, or **people in white coats** but the second of these terms may be considered sexist.

As expedition boffin, he continued with the high altitude physiological research he had begun a year earlier on Cho Oyu.

The latest budget proposals are more generous to science than to almost anything else. Nevertheless, there is discontent among the men in white coats.

The research emphasis does not mean that Glaxo employs thousands of people in white coats searching for the answer to the world's major illnesses.

8 Researchers and their research. Match the two parts of these research report extracts.

1 This is the start of NASA's 10-year programme to pick up the first radio signals from an alien civilisation.

2 The 'vinegar syndrome' that rots movie film stored in sealed cans has been beaten at last.

3 These molluscs, with their beautifully spiralled shells, suffered a catastrophic extinction. So what killed the ammonites?   **extinction 45** ⇓

4 Electrons behave as waves when viewed on extremely small scales.   **electron 140** ⇓

5 Massive oil spills not only harm wildlife, they also do psychological damage to the human inhabitants of the blighted environment.   **oil spill 37** ⇓
wildlife 44 ⇓
environment 31 ⇓

a A team of Californian researchers has linked severe depression to the wreck of the Exxon Valdez in Alaska three years ago.

b NASA researchers believe contact with other intelligent life will be one of the most significant events in the history of the human race.

c Now researchers working for IBM have detected such waves on a metal surface at room temperature.

d Researchers working for Kodak, which made most of the film now in storage, have found a way of absorbing the chemical that destroys the film base.

e Researchers working in Papua New Guinea think they may have been wiped out when the level of oxygen in the oceans rose dramatically, stimulating the evolution of oxygen-hungry fish that simply out-competed them for resources.

Experimentation

experiment
   carry out an experiment
   conduct an experiment
   do an experiment
   perform an experiment

   field experiment
   thought experiment

experimental

Experiments are scientific tests that are **carried out**, **conducted**, **done**, or **performed** to see what happens to something in particular conditions.

A **field experiment** is one done in real surroundings and not in a laboratory.

A **thought experiment** is done by thinking about a problem, rather than experimenting on it.

The related adjective is **experimental**.

◆ **LANGUAGE NOTE**
Experiment can also be used as an uncount noun to refer to experiments in general.

"I've forgotten what this experiment is all about."

Peter Molan of the University of Waikato, Hamilton, has carried out experiments showing that samples of honey are effective against Staphylococcus aureus and other infectious bacteria.

infectious **92** ⇓
bacteria **89** ⇓

Scientists must apply for permits to conduct any experiments involving the manipulation of genes.

gene **109** ⇓

In the early 1900s Pavlov did experiments on learnt-reflex responses. One way of eliminating any doubts about the links between the visual areas discovered in the human brain and those found in monkeys would be to perform the PET imaging experiment on a macaque.

Kareiva applauded the innovative approach of Naeem et al, who carried out experiments on ecosystems under controlled and duplicable conditions. Kareiva is of the view that field experiments on ecosystems will always be necessary, but they tend to be hard to repeat.

ecosystem **32** ⇓

Galileo is said to have dropped two spheres of different weights from the top of the leaning tower of Pisa to demonstrate that the spheres would strike the ground together. But, in fact, he deduced this first using a thought experiment.

Berlin's underground system has become a giant experimental maze, where the experimental animals are human. As part of a project for the whole system, 'scientifically designed' signs have been put up to guide passengers through the city's labyrinthine Alexanderplatz station.

| experimentation experimenter | Doing experiments is **experimentation**, and the people who do them are **experimenters**. |

Lots of computer viruses tend to occur for the first time on university campuses. Now that may be a result of <u>experimentation</u>, but we haven't been able to prove that.

virus 89 ⇓

While the ape is watching, the psychologist puts an apple in Box A and a banana in Box B. The chimpanzee is distracted. When she looks again, the <u>experimenter</u> is eating the banana.

9 **The use of experiments.** Complete this article from *The Economist* with the listed words. (a occurs six times and b, c, and d once each.)

a experiment
b experimentally
c experimenter
d experiments

Tests of the Truth

What do the following have in common? A hundred million dollars' worth of electronics buried under the Illinois prairies, an electric current passing through a schoolgirl's test tubes in the Canary Islands, and the build-up of carbon dioxide in the atmosphere? They can all be described as _____ (1).

The CDF detector at Fermilab is trying to measure the mass of an elusive sub-atomic particle called the top quark; the child in Las Palmas is being taught about the chemistry of oxygen and hydrogen; the build-up of carbon dioxide in the atmosphere is a huge unplanned climatic _____ (2).

mass 137 ⇓
particle 140 ⇓

The aim of science is to find reliable knowledge about the world. The reliability that people have come to expect from the natural sciences comes, in large part, from _____ (3).

Some sciences, such as astronomy, tend to concern themselves more with observation than _____ (4) as such. But they all rely on physical laws that have been, to some extent and at some point, _____ (5) tested.

astronomy 153 ⇓

In principle, the difference between an _____ (6) and a simple observation is this: in an _____ (7) some aspect of nature is under the control of the _____ (8). ...

The most influential account of science this century is that given by Sir Karl Popper. Sir Karl claims that there is an asymmetry between truth and falsehood; no statements can be proved true but some statements can be proved false. Science, he continued, is defined by this falsifiability: it is the fact that they can be proved false, but have not been, which gives accepted scientific statements their value. In this view of science, controlled _____ (9) seems to take on primary importance. ...

Experimental approaches

laboratory bench
test tube
guinea pig

A table used for conducting experiments is a **laboratory bench**. A **test tube** is a small tube-shaped container used in experiments. These terms are often used to talk about processes that take place in the laboratory, but not yet in 'real' contexts, as the second and fourth examples indicate.

If people are used as **guinea pigs** in an experiment, something is tested on them, perhaps for the first time. This expression may show disapproval, as in the example.

◆ **LANGUAGE NOTE**
   Test tube is also spelled with a hyphen.

One day the Data Discman will be a very useful tool on the desk top or <u>laboratory bench</u> as well as in the briefcase.

It can take a decade or more to get a drug from <u>laboratory bench</u> to marketplace.

drug 87 ⇓

...Harry Eagle, a scientist whose discovery of a method for growing human cells in <u>test tubes</u> opened the way for new research into viruses, genetic defects and cancers.

cell 112 ⇓
genetic defect 120 ⇓
cancer 101 ⇓
virus 89 ⇓

Drugs that attack the virus at the same point in its life-cycle as AZT have yet to show in patients the same promise they have in the <u>test tube</u>.

America's Food and Drug Administration often does not approve a drug until it has first been accepted in another large market. The British may not like becoming <u>guinea pigs</u> for new drugs.

sample
specimen

population

control
   control group

replicate
reproduce

validity

Experiments may be conducted on **samples** or **specimens**: examples of a larger amount of something or a larger **population** of individuals.

A **control** or **control group** is used to compare what happens to samples or individuals that are not experimented on with what happens to samples or individuals that are.

The **validity**, or reality, of experimental results is tested by repeating the experiment to see if the results obtained are the same: to see if they can be **replicated** or **reproduced**.

replicate 117 ⇓

It would help if researchers from different laboratories could team up and <u>replicate</u> each other's experiments on different <u>samples</u> of the same fossils. But here again there is another problem: some of the <u>specimens</u> are extremely rare.

"IGNORE HIM. HE'S A HYPOCHONDRIAC."

They went on to test 850 blood samples from people living in three locations in the US and Israel, and found the mutation in 1 per cent of the samples. In other <u>populations</u>, mutations are found in only 1 in 500 people.   **mutation 118** ⇓

They studied 105 samples of brain tissue from five people who had died of Alzheimer's and two elderly people who had died from other causes, whose brain tissues were used as <u>controls</u>.   **tissue 82** ⇓

They found that while healthy men taking drugs to lower their blood cholesterol levels were less likely to die of heart attacks than men in <u>control groups</u>, the drug takers were more likely to die from cancer, accidents, suicide and murder.

Enclosure (not necessarily full closure) paves the way to an experimental approach in ecology that is more receptive to advanced instrumentation,   **ecology 31** ⇓

and consequently offers a better control over experimental conditions, and allows quantification of the observations and a powerful exploration of their <u>validity</u> by means of comparison and repetition.

Research has shown that limiting calorie intake has an effect on reducing the incidence of almost all diseases associated with ageing: heart disease, stroke, as well as cancer. They have <u>reproduced</u> these results in every other species they have tested.   **disease 81** ⇓

10 **Missing link.** Which two-word expression from this section is missing from all these extracts?

drug came into use; others are under study in the	.... Ornidyl, approved for widespread use last
body as they do in carefully selected cells in the	.... Clinical trials should show the effectiveness
Tom Donohue. Many things work in vitro (in the	...............) that do not work in vivo (in people). In fact
makes studying Tamandron's potential difficult in the	.... However, he hopes that the work he and
The discovery that hair cells can be grown in the	.... is not the only reason for optimism. The past
of such a major milestone, the recreation in the	.... , no less, of molecular evolution according to
mice essential. They form the link between the	.... and the patient. When people have ethical

Observation and hypothesis

phenomenon

observe
observation

measurement

data
  analyse data
  collect data
  gather data
  interpret data
  process data
  raw data

analysis

conclude
conclusion

evidence

A **phenomenon** is something that is seen to occur or exist: it is **observed**.

Information obtained by making **observations** and making **measurements** of them is **data**.

Data is **collected** or **gathered**. It is then **processed** and **analysed** in a process of **analysis**. Unprocessed, unanalysed data is **raw data**.

Scientists look for meaning in data: they **interpret** it in order to reach **conclusions** or to **conclude** things. Data and other information form the **evidence** for these conclusions.

data 53 ⇓

◆ **LANGUAGE NOTE**
The plural of **phenomenon** is **phenomena**.
The form **data** can be used as a singular or plural. Sometimes **datum** is used for the singular.
Analyse is spelled **analyze** in American English.

Scientists find chaotic dynamics useful in explaining <u>observed phenomena</u> such as the way populations grow.

Fleming made the initial <u>observations</u>, but Ernst Chain and Howard Florey developed the first antibiotic.

antibiotic 94 ⇓

The new experiments are an attempt to explain high levels of ozone in the troposphere across much of the southern hemisphere during parts of the year. This phenomenon was revealed in 1990 by <u>data collected</u> by NASA satellites.

satellite 157 ⇓

Rather than spend weeks cruising the ocean <u>gathering data</u>, a pair of researchers have scaled down the ocean and rebuilt it in their laboratory.

The report criticises NASA's insistence that all <u>raw data</u> from the EOSDOS satellites must be <u>processed</u> into a single standardised format.

The study of lifestyle threw up overwhelming <u>evidence</u>. 'When we <u>analysed</u> the <u>data</u>, we were able to <u>conclude</u> that smoking was emphatically a cause of lung cancer.'

cancer 101 ⇓

The data were pooled for statistical analysis with a single datum included for each bird.

At the time, it was believed that 85 per cent of the fuel was in the reactor shaft. This was based on measurements made in 1986, but the data were interpreted incorrectly.

Jacobsen based his conclusion on an analysis of the decay of samarium-147 into neodymium-143, which has a half-life of 106 billion years.

half-life 145 ⇓

hypothesis
test a hypothesis
hypothesize
empirical

An experiment may be done to **test a hypothesis**: to see whether a suggested explanation for something is true.

Approaching scientific problems by **hypothesizing** about them and testing these hypotheses by observation and experimentation is often described as being **empirical**.

◆ **LANGUAGE NOTE**

Hypothesize is also spelled **hypothesise** in British English.
The plural of **hypothesis** is **hypotheses**, and its related adjective is **hypothetical**.

One of the study's tasks is to test the hypothesis that 10 years of a diet very low in fat and high in fruits and vegetables will lower the incidence of breast cancer in women.

So it seems that galaxies weigh more than the sum of their visible parts. To solve the problem of this 'missing mass', scientists have hypothesised the existence of all sorts of mysterious 'dark matter'.

galaxy 177 ⇓

mass 137 ⇓

Geology has moved out of the archive and into the laboratory. Students are now taught to collect data, design hypotheses, erect models and test them against more data.

'Lindahl fails in basic scientific technique,' charges Golenberg. 'You are supposed to generate hypotheses and then test them against empirical observations. Instead, he tests the validity of the observations against the hypothesis. In other words, Lindahl states that he knows DNA cannot survive longer than a few tens of thousands of years, so any claims for longer preservations must be wrong.'

DNA 111 ⇓

11 **Disputed parenthood.** Read this article from the *New Scientist* and answer the questions.

Seeing biology through Aristotle's eyes

We generally chart the start of modern science as we know it from Francis Bacon, one of the major English figures of the Renaissance period. It is Bacon, writing in the first decades of the 17th century, who is usually credited with spelling out the principles of empirical science and the role that experiments should play in hypothesis testing.

The great irony, however, is that, despite his enormous influence on scientists from Newton onwards, Bacon never himself touched a test tube. He simply set the scene from his armchair and told scientists how they ought to proceed.

In fact, the real credit for establishing genuine empirical science based on careful observation and deduction of causal explanations belongs to Aristotle. ...

For Bacon, Aristotle is the big baddy who was single-handedly responsible for all the worst habits of the intellectual trivialisers of the medieval period. But if Bacon genuinely thought this, it must have been because he never bothered to read Aristotle at first hand.

For even the most casual perusal of Aristotle's writings reveals a formidable intellect spanning everything from moral and political theory to logic, physics and biology. And it is in his biology that Aristotle's genius really shines through. Unlike his physics, Aristotle's biology is marked by an extreme emphasis on observation. ... Aristotle's biology has stood the test of time in a way that his physics (which very conspicuously lacks an empirical dimension) has not. ...

1 If someone is credited for something, are they said to be responsible for it?

2 If you spell something out, do you specify it?

3 Was Bacon an experimenter?

4 What is the verb related to 'deduction'? a) deduct, b) deduce, or c) dedicate.

5 Does 'trivialise' show approval?

6 Does the writer think Bacon actually read Aristotle?

7 Does 'formidable' show approval?

8 Which was Aristotle's 'best' subject?   **physics 129** ⇓

9 Was Aristotle's physics empirical?

10 Is Aristotle's biology still of value scientifically?

Reasoning and intuition

logic
logical
reasoning
deduce
deduction
deductive
infer
inference

If you **deduce** or **infer** something, you come to the conclusion that it is true because of other things you know are true.

Deduction and **inference** can refer both to a conclusion and to the process of reaching it.

Reasoning like this is **deductive** in its **logic** and may be described as **logical**.

'Using and Applying Mathematics' requires pupils to initiate mathematical investigations, to choose applications and to apply <u>reasoning</u>, <u>logic</u> and proof to their work.

Crick and Watson were working far more from <u>logical</u> reasoning about how genetics should work than from laboratory data about how it did work.   **genetics 106** ⇓

The eclipses revealed that Pluto's diameter is 2,300 km and Charon's diameter is 1,190 km. These figures were used to <u>deduce</u> the volume of each object.

In economics, hypotheses are generated by a process of logical <u>deduction</u> from sets of initial assumptions about the behaviour of consumers, producers, etc.

He referred to 'those students who agree in thinking that the science of <u>deductive</u> economics is in its infancy'.

Wolpoff has been strongly critical of using DNA data to <u>infer</u> patterns of human history.   **DNA 111** ⇓

The enlarged areas of the brain are known to be involved in dealing with language. So a clear <u>inference</u> can be made. Too many brain cells in the right hemisphere, along with too much cross-talk between the hemispheres, is confusing the part of the left hemisphere that deals with language.   **cell 112** ⇓

intuit
intuition
intuitive
hunch
counter–intuitive

If you **intuit** something, you feel that it is true even if you have incomplete or no evidence for it. **Intuition** can refer both to the feeling that something is true as well as the process of thinking in this way. Thinking like this is **intuitive**. An intuition is, informally, a **hunch**.

Something that is **counter–intuitive** does not seem reasonable.

Some mathematicians are worried by a recent trend that permits 'theoretical' mathematicians to <u>intuit</u> ideas and not worry too much about their rigorous proof.

…his telling of the discovery of PAS, which reads more like a spiritual vision based on scientific <u>intuition</u>, rather than a methodical piece of deduction.

A scientist with no imagination would find it impossible to form new hypotheses against which to test results, and the <u>intuitive</u> leap that produces an explanation for previously inexplicable phenomena is arguably a form of applied <u>hunch</u>.

Another major theme is that of quantum theory. The puzzling nature of the theory is underlined from its earliest development, especially its <u>counter-intuitive</u> aspects.

quantum theory 137 ⇓

12 **Reasoning or intuition?** Which word is missing from each of these sentences: reasoning or intuition? (Each word occurs three times.)

1 Computers are better at mathematics, and at precisely specifiable scientific _____ , than many humans are.

2 Experiments do not always need laboratories and equipment. With thought experiments, scientists can rely on pure _____ to make a discovery about nature, or to expose a paradox or inconsistency within accepted theories, without ever lifting a test tube.

3 'My _____ told me that would be a problem,' he says. 'I had no evidence for saying that, just a gut feeling.'

4 White saw in the universities too little faith in _____ , too much faith in the intellect.

5 The breakthrough came about, not through theory, but because Whitcomb, was, as another aeronautical engineer commented, 'a guy who just has a sense of _____ about these kinds of aeronautical problems. He sort of feels what the air wants to do.'

6 The most widely used aptitude tests are designed to measure your ability in verbal, numerical and diagrammatic _____ .

Theory and theories

| theory |
| theoretical |
| theorist |
| theoretician |
| |
| model |

A **theory** is an idea or set of ideas designed to explain something. The related adjective is **theoretical**. People who produce and work on theories are **theorists** or **theoreticians**.

A **model** of a phenomenon, system, or process is a theoretical description of it, designed to aid understanding of how it works.

◆ **LANGUAGE NOTE**

Theory is also used as an uncount noun to talk about the theories of a particular area as a whole, as in the second example.

Model is also used as a verb: scientists model phenomena, systems, and processes, for example on a computer.

If two alternative <u>theories</u> explain the same phenomenon, the simpler theory is the more useful.

<u>Theory</u> tells us that temperature measurements need to be repeated every five years to pick up warnings of real climate change.

climate change 46 ⇓

A key feature of the scientific method is that the <u>theorist</u> can make a definite prediction of the value of some measurable quantity, and the experimenter can then go ahead and check it to some level of accuracy.

Whatever happens when S-L9 crashes into Jupiter in July, it will be duly recorded from sites around the world. The instruments and methods that will be used in observing the event are being designed to measure what <u>theoreticians</u> predict will happen.

molecule 131 ⇓

Benson and Siebert used experimental data for ice and for pairs of water molecules in the gas phase to construct a <u>theoretical</u> <u>model</u> of liquid water.

gas 132 ⇓
liquid 132 ⇓

Kevin Zahnle of NASA Ames Research Center has <u>modelled</u> the motion of meteorites travelling through the thick Venusian atmosphere.

meteorite 170 ⇓

"WHAT WE ESPECIALLY LIKE ABOUT THESE THEORETICAL TYPES IS THAT THEY DON'T TIE UP THOUSANDS OF DOLLARS WORTH OF EQUIPMENT."

13 **A theory of theories.** Put the sections of this *New Scientist* review of *Betting on Theories* by Patrick Maher into the correct order. (The first section is a and the last is g.)

Do Scientists Play Dice?

a Dinosaurs were wiped out by a meteorite. The universe began in a big bang singularity. Electrons are quantum-wave particles. Species evolve through chance mutation and natural selection.

universe *153* ⇓
big bang *179* ⇓
electron *140* ⇓
particle *140* ⇓
species *45* ⇓
evolve *118* ⇓
mutation *118* ⇓

b At first sight, the answers appear self-evident. A theory is deduced as a plausible explanation of facts derived from observation or experiment.

c But how do scientists confirm their theories? When does a theory pass from suggestive hypothesis to unassailable truth? How do scientists choose between rival theories? Philosophers of science have been worrying away at these questions for years.

d Emissions of greenhouse gases cause global climate change. Gravity is the local distortion of space-time by mass. All ravens are black.

emission *46* ⇓
greenhouse gases
46 ⇓
gravity *148* ⇓
space-time *150* ⇓
mass *137* ⇓

e Some scientific theories merely satisfy our curiosity; others form the foundations of understanding upon which our very survival depends or are the basis of billion-dollar industries.

f Whatever their significance, scientific theories are absolutely fundamental to Western science-based culture and civilisation.

g It gains credibility through the further accumulation of evidence confirming its expectations or predictions. It gains in credibility if the new evidence is not anticipated by rival theories. ...

Laws of science

equation
formula

proof

theorem
  formulate a theorem
law
  formulate a law
principle
  formulate a principle

A statement in mathematics or logic that is the product of reasoning is a **theorem**. The explanation of this reasoning is the theorem's **proof**, often in the form of a series of **equations**.

A **formula** is a series of mathematical, chemical, or other symbols that express a scientific rule.

General statements that are confirmed by observation are **principles** or **laws**.

Theorems, principles, and laws are often preceded by the name of the person who first **formulated** them.

◆ **LANGUAGE NOTE**
The plural of **formula** is **formulae** or **formulas**.

Certain painters, like Piero della Francesca and Juan Gris, were truly obsessed by mathematical formulae. To such scientific painters, the arithmetic of proportion outweighs any other element of art.

Minkowski also realised that the equations that describe such curious phenomena as, for example, the way moving clocks run slower and moving objects get smaller, are, in essence, the familiar equations of Pythagoras's theorem, extended to four dimensions.

…the proof that there exist languages that cannot be recognised by a Turing machine (a theoretical universal computer), the proof being similar to a proof of Godel's theorem that all consistent logical systems are incomplete.

It's called the Copernican principle. Copernicus discovered that there was nothing special about the position of the earth.

Science requires the formulation of laws based upon experimental observations made under different conditions using deductive logic. There is no archaeological law comparable with Newton's laws of motion and repeated definitions are often not possible. Under this definition, archaeology is not a science.

14 Laws and theorems. Match the two parts of these extracts.

1 The basis of Bayes' theorem is that if the outcome of one event is known, this affects the probability of another event occurring.

2 Pythagoras's theorem was independently discovered many times by different thinkers

3 It is a commonplace observation that work expands to fill the time available for its completion.

4 The team divided DNA sequences into short 'words' of arbitrary length and counted the number of times each word occurred in the complete sequence. **DNA 111 ⇓**

5 Hardware follows the law postulated by Intel co-founder Gordon Moore, which states that computing power available for a given price doubles every two years. **computing 53 ⇓**

6 In this picture, which is now known as Mach's principle, the resistance to motion – or inertia – **inertia 137 ⇓**

7 Hubble's law says that a galaxy which is twice **galaxy 177 ⇓**

a (although Pythagoras was probably not one of them).

b as far away as another is moving away from us at twice the speed.

c For example, there might be a one-in-five chance of frost on March nights, and a one-in-fifty chance of snow. But if there was frost on the previous night, the chances of having snow are modified.

d Software development, however, is governed by the rule known as Hofstadter's law: It always takes longer than you expect, even when you take into account Hofstadter's law. **software 63 ⇓**

e They found a pattern of word frequencies that closely matched that seen in human languages, a pattern known as Zipf's law.

f With those words *The Economist* coined Parkinson's Law in 1955, naming it after the author of the article, Professor C Northcote Parkinson.

g we feel when we try to push an object is a result of trying to make it accelerate relative to the distribution of all the matter in the Universe. **accelerate 137 ⇓**
matter 129 ⇓
universe 153 ⇓

Presenting findings

publish
  publish an article
  publish a paper
  publish findings
  publish results

publication

article
  submit an article

submission

journal

Scientists usually **publish** their **results** or **findings** in **articles** or **papers** in scientific **journals**.

Articles and papers are **submitted** to journals for assessment before **publication**. Articles are submitted in a process of **submission**.

Luigi Galvani, a professor of anatomy, discovered by accident that electricity could move frogs' legs. He published his findings in 1791.

The researchers are blocking publication of a paper by a rival group which reanalyses results generated by the Fermilab's Tevatron particle collider.

particle *140* ⇓

In the test, volunteers were presented with a child one metre tall and an adult 1.8 metres tall. The volunteer 'drivers' were asked to stop a safe distance in front of the pedestrian. Describing their results in the journal 'Perception', the researchers say that drivers were more likely to make errors when the image was a child's.

The Director of the Office of Scientific Integrity, Lyle Bivens, said Mr Gallo was guilty of deliberate deception when he claimed in 1984 that he had grown the Aids virus without French help. He had overridden objections from fellow scientists before the article was submitted to 'Science' magazine. They wanted the French to be given more credit, but Mr Gallo had deliberately deleted all references.

virus *89* ⇓

For some years it has been common practice for everyone working on an experiment to be named on all the papers published. As a result, the vast majority of authors on a given paper do not write a single word of it, make no direct contribution to the published results and most likely do not even read it until after submission.

conference
congress
meeting

paper
  deliver a paper
  give a paper
  present a paper

Scientists may give presentations of their work at **conferences** or **congresses**: gatherings of scientists who meet to discuss their work. These and other types of scientific gatherings are referred to as **meetings**.

If someone **delivers**, **gives**, or **presents a paper** at a meeting such as this, they make an oral presentation.

In a paper presented at an international congress on refrigeration in Montreal last year, Raymond Solomon from the American chip company Intel says that by the year 2000 a typical processor chip may have as many as 100 million transistors and generate 20 watts of heat.

chip *58* ⇓

Adults who survive childhood leukaemia after radiation therapy do not have an increased risk of having children with severe birth defects, say the American researchers who presented their findings to a conference on genetics held in Paris last week.

radiation *139* ⇓

genetics *106* ⇓

Barbara Brown delivered a paper at the Frankfurt meeting in which she showed that dental morphology in Homo erectus is little different in early African specimens nearly 2 million years old and Chinese specimens about 0.5 million years old.

Addressing the conference, Boris Turukhano gave a paper on storing information in holograms.

15 Lines of communication. Complete the sentences using appropriate grammatical forms of words from the article from *The Economist* below. (The number of letters in each missing word is indicated in brackets.)

1 Before an article is published in a journal, it is assessed by people who know about the subject in a process of _____ review. Someone who assesses an article in this way is a _____ . (4 and 7)

2 Two informal expressions relating to the way that results are communicated unofficially are _____ _____ and _____ . (6, 4 and 9)

3 If information is communicated to a large number of people, it is _____ . (12)

4 If information is communicated when it should not be, it is _____ . (6)

5 Information, perhaps about someone's private life, communicated informally, is _____ . (6)

6 If something is formally approved, it is _____ . (8)

7 A place for storing information that is no longer being actively used is an _____ . (7)

Breaking the News

...Except in the jealous, competitive world of molecular biology, publication in a journal has become mere ratification of a result that has already been well disseminated and, as it were, pre-peer-reviewed. John Maddox, the editor of *Nature* says that for physicists at least he is becoming little more than an archive for results everyone knows already. ...

physicist 129 ⇓

Whereas the telephone had much less effect on research than on other professions, electronic mail has produced a sort of computer logorrhea. Everything from a result to a piece of gossip is passed through this ubiquitous, international rumour mill.

electronic mail 72 ⇓

One effect of this fast and effective grapevine is that fads and fashions sweep through fields faster. ...The pace has quickened, but the need to be first, on the grounds that no one remembers the second person to make a discovery, has not relaxed. As a result, scientists now sometimes announce their results at press conferences, short-circuiting the laborious - and leaky - system of peer review.

Paul Chu of the University of Houston, sent to a journal his announcement of a new superconductor with what many people think was a deliberate error in the chemical formula: ytterbium instead of yttrium. The incorrect formula did leak, perhaps via one of the referees whom the journal asked to assess the paper, proving the leakiness. ...

superconductor 135 ⇓

Discoveries and breakthroughs

discover
discoverer
discovery
    make a discovery

The **discoverer** of something is the person who finds it or becomes aware of it for the first time by **discovering** it or by **making a discovery**.

Wallace was the co-discoverer with Darwin of the process of evolution by natural selection.

evolution **118** ⇓

Neuroscience stands today roughly where atomic physics was in 1919, when Ernest Rutherford discovered the nucleus, or where molecular biology stood in 1944 when Oswald Avery proved that genetic material was made of DNA.

physics **129** ⇓
nucleus **140** ⇓
DNA **111** ⇓

An ink pen running at regular intervals over a paper chart was the hint that led Jocelyn Bell Burnell to make an astonishing discovery about the universe. Nobody yelled 'eureka'. At the time, she was a 24-year-old PhD student at Cambridge, doing a routine monitoring job. But she rapidly acquired an international reputation for her discovery of the pulsar, a new type of star.

universe **153** ⇓
pulsar **177** ⇓
star **175** ⇓

breakthrough

break new ground
ground-breaking

pioneer
pioneering work

A discovery may be described as a **breakthrough**. People may say that it is **ground-breaking** or that it **breaks new ground**.

Scientists who are the first to do work in a particular area are **pioneers**. They are said to **pioneer** particular developments or do **pioneering work** in a particular area.

"I CAN HELP YOU WITH TINY, LITTLE STEPS. AS FOR BREAKTHROUGHS, YOU'RE ON YOUR OWN."

The sheet of material, about 5mm square, exhibits all the properties of a superconductor. However, Tomoji Kawai says that more tests are needed to confirm their findings. Japanese physicists hailed the discovery as a breakthrough.

superconductor **135** ⇓

physicist **129** ⇓

In the 1940s, Griffin made the ground-breaking discovery, with his colleague Robert Galambos, that bats use radar navigation.

Where their report breaks new ground is in demonstrating that the longer-term climate shifts seen in earlier records are themselves marked by strong variations of less than ten years' duration.

climate change **46** ⇓

The team were well aware that the pioneers who studied nearby galaxies in the 1930s and 1940s mistook growing nebulae and star clusters for individual stars.

galaxy **177** ⇓
nebula **175** ⇓

Hodgkin <u>pioneered</u> the use of computers to handle the complex mathematics involved in determining crystal structures by X-ray crystallography.

crystal 135 ⇓

The general theory of relativity predicts that for any given mass, there is a critical radius known as the Schwarzschild radius, named after the <u>pioneering work</u> of Karl Schwarzschild in 1916. Once any mass is squeezed within the confines of its Schwarzschild radius, space-time is curved so tightly around the mass by its own gravity that it is cut off from the gravity outside and becomes a black hole.

relativity 150 ⇓
mass 137 ⇓
space-time 150 ⇓
gravity 148 ⇓
black hole 177 ⇓

16 **Legendary exploits.** Read this review from the *New Scientist* of a book called *British Medicine in an Age of Reform* and answer the questions.

Medical Mythology

...One of the problems with science and medicine is still the extent to which they have a mythology instead of a history. It is full of stereotyped pioneers breaking new ground and noble images of heroes, even heroines.

The purpose of this mythology is not hard to find. It clearly attempts to buttress the mythology that emerging professions like to have of themselves. In an excellent essay, Perry Williams looks at the mythology of nursing and promptly demolishes it in favour of a straightforward account of how modern nursing developed.

Most telling is his entirely convincing account of how the Florence Nightingale myth has worked against the interests of nurses. He replaces the image of the selfless, caring woman on the Crimean wards with that of the ruthless, determined reformer of hospital building, administration and standards of hygiene. 'The lady with the lamp' becomes the woman holding the new broom and the bucket of disinfectant. ...

medicine 80 ⇓

1 Is 'stereotyped' used showing approval?

2 If X buttresses Y, does it support Y?
3 Is an emerging profession one that has been recognized for a long time?
4 Which of these things can also be demolished? a) arguments, b) meals, c) houses.
5 Does 'straightforward' indicate approval?

6 If an account is telling, is it revealing?
7 Why does this myth work against the interests of nurses?

8 If someone reforms something they bring about c _ _ _ _ _ s .

9 What do new brooms do, metaphorically speaking?

Crossword

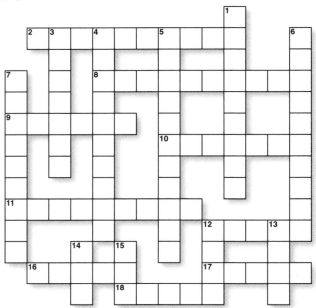

Across

2 Relating to science (10)

8 Thing observed with an unusual plural (10)

9 Idea about why something is like it is (6)

10 Submit this to a journal (7)

11 Something that a technophile would like (9)

12 What a scientist does with a hypothesis: he or she _____ it (5)

16 Nothing is better than this: _____ of the art (5)

17 The problem is to get from the laboratory _____ to 'real' applications (5)

18 Stereotypical colour of scientific wear (5)

Down

1 A geologist is an earth _____ (9)

3 Scientists gather or _____ data (7)

4 Noun or verb for trying things out (10)

5 New products or ideas (11)

6 Scientific gatherings (10)

7 Not deductive, but useful even so (9)

12 Second half of experimental equipment (4)

13 This can be high or hi (4)

14 Scientific rule (3)

15 Ground-breaking adjective (3)

Ecology and the environment

environment
environmental
environmentally
  environmentally aware

ecology
ecological

The **environment** is the earth's land, sea, and atmosphere. The related adjective is **environmental**.

environment *108* ⇓
environmental *108* ⇓

The related adverb is **environmentally**. Someone who is **environmentally aware** is sensitive to the environment.

Ecology is the scientific study of the environment. The ecology of a particular place is the balance of relationships between plants, animals, people, and the environment there. Ecology is also used to refer to political and ideological movements, as in the fourth example. The related adjective is **ecological**.

The government hopes to spend 7 billion yen next year to develop technologies which protect the environment.

According to the California Assembly Office of Research, the region's cars cause $4.7 billion in environmental damage.

Unfortunately, while many trekkers are environmentally aware, some are oblivious of the damage they can cause.

Although ecology may indeed be turning into an 'earth science', it is clear that there is still room for the small-scale laboratory or field experiment.

laboratory *11* ⇑
field experiment *13* ⇑

Ecology is the great hope of the 21st century just as socialism symbolises the idealism of the 20th century.

He co-ordinated a pioneering study of the ecology of Hong Kong. Researchers monitored a range of biological and cultural factors.

pioneering *28* ⇑

We know that the use of pesticides may affect the ecological or biological balance of the environment.

ecologist

Ecologists are scientists who study the environment.

environmentalist

Environmentalists are people, not necessarily scientists, who are concerned about the environment.

When you're surrounded by rainforest, you can't not be affected by it. It's a powerful feeling, all those organisms interacting in the most bizarre and complex ways. That's why I became an <u>ecologist</u>.

The most radical governor is Gilberto Mestrinho of Amazonas, Brazil's largest state. <u>Environmentalists</u>, he claims, 'want to keep the Amazon like a circus, with us as the monkeys.'

1 Environmental pairs. The words in the box often come after 'environmental'. Match the words in the box to the words a-g, which have similar meanings.

a activists   c considerations   e expenses   g questions
b advantages   d effect   f laws

campaigners

legislation   issues

environmental

benefits   impact

costs   factors

Eco-terms

eco-	The prefix **eco–** is often used in words to mean 'environment-' or 'environmentally-'.
eco-friendly eco-label eco-tourism eco-tourist	For example, an **eco-friendly** product or activity is one that does not damage the environment, or does less damage than a normal one. Labels on products giving environmental information are **eco-labels**.
ecosystem	**Eco-tourism** is tourism that does not harm the environment, or does less harm than normal tourism; people taking part in it are **eco-tourists**.
	An **ecosystem** is the ecology of a particular area viewed as a system of organisms in a particular environment.

◆ **LANGUAGE NOTE**

Words of this kind beginning **eco–** are also spelled as one word.

Bicycles offer the perfect <u>eco-friendly</u> method of travelling around the vast and beautiful and flat countryside that surrounds Cambridge.

Brands of washing machines which cause least damage to the environment are to carry the first '<u>eco-labels</u>' independently assessed by the European community.

Ecotourism is a boom industry. Wherever wildlife exists in a relatively undisturbed state, from the tropics to the poles, today's environmentally aware tourists are willing to pay large sums to see it. Ecotourists not only pay more, they also ask less.

This is a guided tour through the underwater world of the common pond. Wright describes its intricate ecosystem clearly, a delicate balance of plant and animal life.

2 Eco-exercise. 'Eco-' is used in front of many other adjectives and nouns to form new words. Match these definitions to the words listed. (Each word is used once.)

1 authorities with the power to police pollution

2 studying the environmental impact of a company's activities

3 goods that do not damage the environment

4 radical environmentalists using confrontational tactics

5 doing things in ways that are environmentally efficient

6 an environmentally-friendly city

a eco-audit	c eco-cops	e eco-products
b eco-city	d eco-efficiency	f eco-warriors

Now use these words to complete the extracts.

i Her hatred of cars stems from the death of her mother in a road accident. She now describes herself as a worshipper of Mother Earth and lives with other eco-_____ in an encampment beside the proposed A30 route near Exeter.

ii Product performance is key in winning over consumers. With neither consumer demand nor government regulation, there is little incentive to pioneer new eco-_____

pioneer 28 ⇑

iii But eco-friendly firms are not willing to put themselves at a disadvantage by allowing their competitors to get away with environmental pollution. These firms are as keen as the eco-_____ to see stiff anti-pollution laws approved and enforced.

iv Eco-_____ is the combining of economic and environmental factors. It means that being efficient in terms of the environment can also mean being efficient in economic terms.

v Mestrinho also announced that his government was planning to build an eco-_____ for tourists in the heart of the rainforest. He said the city would be a type of ecological Disneyland.

vi What an eco-_____ is going to mean is that each company will have a committee to look at the environmental impacts that a business may have.

Pollution

pollutant
pollute
polluter
pollution

Pollutants are substances, especially man-made chemicals and waste products, that negatively affect, or **pollute**, the environment.

This process is **pollution**; countries, organizations, or individuals responsible for it are **polluters**.

It was discovered that fumes from the phosphorus enter the body, causing necrosis or 'phossy jaw' gangrene in the lower jawbone. This disease killed and maimed thousands of match workers, a classic example of an industrial <u>pollutant</u> damaging the workforce.

disease 81 ⇓

Motor vehicles, already the main source of city air <u>pollution</u> in rich countries, will increasingly <u>pollute</u> poor cities, too.

Western Europe's biggest <u>polluter</u>, Germany, also spends the most cleaning up the environment.

refuse
waste

effluent

dump

Pollutants include:

waste from industry and households. Waste is referred to formally as **refuse**.

effluent: industrial and human waste released into rivers and the sea.

If waste material is intentionally put somewhere it is **dumped**. The place where it is put is a **dump**.

◆ **LANGUAGE NOTE**
   Waste is a noun, as in the first example, and an adjective, as in the second.

34

Legislation has usually attacked air and water pollution first and solid <u>waste</u> last.

A report says that the 13 million cars scrapped annually in Europe, including about 1.3 million in Britain, are creating a mountain of polluting <u>waste</u> plastics, rubber, oils and glass.

Marpol, the world maritime regulatory agency, banned the dumping of all plastic <u>refuse</u>, including golf balls, into the sea in 1989, following studies that found bags, six-pack holders and other refuse in the guts of sea creatures.

The state says the company acted recklessly when it <u>dumped</u> nearly 22,000 tons of toxic waste in an abandoned canal bed.

We should stop treating the sea as a <u>dump</u> for human and industrial <u>effluent</u>.

biodegradable	Materials that break down naturally when dumped without causing harm to the environment are **biodegradable**.
recyclable **recycle** **recycling**	Materials that can be reused, usually after some form of industrial reprocessing, are **recyclable** and people are encouraged to **recycle** them in a process of **recycling**.

◆ LANGUAGE NOTE

All these words can also be spelled with hyphens.

What is popularly thought of as <u>biodegradable</u> is usually well-preserved. Why promote biodegradable plastics made of corn-starch? If the bugs will not eat corn on the cob, they won't eat corn starch in plastics.

The packaging industry proposes to issue each household with a separate bin for <u>recyclable</u> waste products.

'There are three Rs in environmental waste management - reduce, reuse and <u>recycle</u>,' says Kumamoto. 'The new bill tries to promote <u>recycling</u>, but it doesn't promote reuse and reduce.'

3 **Disposal exercise.** Read the article below from *The Economist* and complete the sentences. (The number of letters in each missing word is indicated in brackets.)

1   Throwing waste away is referred to as waste _____ . (8)

2   If you get rid of waste, you _____ of it. (7)

3   A place on land where waste is put is a _____ . (8)

4   Waste is burnt in an _____ . (11)

5   Dangerous waste is _____ . (9)

Throwing things away

What people buy today, they throw away tomorrow. But finding somewhere to put the rubbish is becoming harder and more expensive. America's Environmental Protection Agency estimates that 80 per cent of the country's landfills will shut by 2010. Japan looks like running out of landfill space by 2005. Holland has more or less run out already.

Other options are no easier. The Swiss consistently vote against any new incinerators. West Germany, which in 1988 exported 2.1 million tons of rubbish to East Germany has now lost that useful dumping ground. Most industrial countries agreed two years ago to discourage shipments of hazardous waste to the Third World. Britain, which has long burnt the stuff on ships in the North Sea, has promised to stop it by the end of this year. No wonder that rich-country governments increasingly think of waste disposal as their most pressing environmental problem.

The problem is largely man-made. Rarely is there an absolute shortage of space to put more rubbish dumps. But nobody wants a dump, or an incinerator, next door. So the piles of waste grow, while the places to pile them diminish. This affects companies in two ways.

First, getting rid of hazardous waste is becoming more expensive. This is partly because landfill costs have soared; and also because companies now face a lengthy paper-chase, filling in forms that record every stage of their waste's progress, from factory gate to dump. As a result, more and more companies dispose of their own waste; or they (expensively) change the way they work so as to reduce the amount they create.

Secondly, the difficulty of getting rid of ordinary household rubbish is driving some governments to impose new regulations on companies, making them take back their products when the customer wants to be rid of them. That in turn is changing the way companies design products as diverse as cardboard boxes, cars and computers. ...

Leaks and spills

leak
leakage

spill
  oil spill
spillage
  oil spillage

fumes

hazardous

noxious
toxic

acid rain

◆ **LANGUAGE NOTE**
Leak and **spill** are also verbs.

Unintentional or unauthorized releases of chemicals, gases, or oil are **leaks**, **leakages**, **spills**, or **spillages**. Spills from oil tankers are **oil spills** or **oil spillages**. gas 132 ⇓

Releases of poisonous gases are **fumes**.

Substances that present a risk are **hazardous**.

Poisonous substances are **noxious** or **toxic**.

Releases into the atmosphere of gases from industry and car exhausts cause **acid rain** which is harmful to plants and trees.

When Union Carbide's pesticides plant sprang a leak and spewed a toxic cloud of methyl isocynate over Bhopal, some 2,500 people died and hundreds of thousands were injured. injure 82 ⇓

Ever Ready claims that the safety features in the batteries prevent leakages of lithium.

CHEMICAL SPILL AT WASTE SITE. Four people were treated in hospital after a drum of chemical waste burst open at a recycling works in Pontlottyn, South Wales, spreading fumes over a wide area.

…the Exxon Valdez, the tanker that ran aground in Prince William Sound in Alaska in 1989, causing the biggest oil spillage in American history.

Heavy industry pollutes our rivers with noxious chemicals.

He argued that rich countries should dump their toxic and hazardous waste on the poorest, because people in the Third World live shorter lives.

If this coal were to be burnt, it would produce unacceptably high levels of sulphur dioxide, a major source of pollution and acid rain.

37

4 **Forms of pollution.** Complete the extracts with the listed items. (Each item is used once.)

a acid rain   c leakages   e spills
b fumes   d leaked   f toxic

1 The burning of 'sea coal' led to complaints about the effect that smoke and _____ in the city were having on people's health.

2 The worsening weather conditions provoked more fears of _____ from the vessel, which has already lost an estimated 1,000 tons of crude oil.

3 Massive oil _____ not only harm wildlife, they also cause psychological damage to the human inhabitants of the blighted environment.

4 Safe disposal of a 55-gallon drum of _____ waste costs up to $1,000.

5 Sweden raised the alarm about _____ , explaining that smoke produced by British and German coal was sterilising its lakes.

6 The report says that these abandoned vehicles will pollute the desert with rust, _____ fuel and heavy metals.

Contamination and the food chain

contaminate
contamination

food chain

When the environment is affected by pollutants, it is **contaminated**.

Contamination may enter the **food chain**: the series of living things where each living thing is food for the next living thing in the series.

HOW SALMON RETURNED TO THE THAMES

Recent US research suggests that up to 30 per cent of underground storage tanks and pipelines leak. One gallon of petrol can <u>contaminate</u> millions of gallons of groundwater.

Land-based pollution is a major source of <u>contamination</u> of the oceans.

Seals in the White Sea and Barents Sea were found to be dying from blood cancer. Autopsies conducted at the Northern Polar Institute in Archangel suggested that pollution was the cause. This is worrying. If seals are at the top of a <u>food chain</u> with a lot of radioactive fish below them, then so are people.

cancer *101* ⇓

5 **Paradise contaminated.** Read this article from the *New Scientist* and answer the questions.

Gold-Diggers Poison Brazil's Wild Paradise

Dangerous levels of mercury have been detected in the Pantanal in southwestern Brazil, the world's largest wetland. Researchers say fish have been found contaminated with 24 times the level of mercury the World Health Organisation considers safe. The mercury is dumped into rivers that flow into the Pantanal by gold-miners who use it to extract the precious metal from silt.

Luiz Marques Vieira, of Embrapa, the government-run Brazilian agricultural research institute, says the findings are extremely serious. He says the contamination has entered the food chain of the Paraguay river and could affect the countries through which it flows: Paraguay, Argentina and Bolivia. Mercury accumulates in the body and leads to blindness and death. Some people in the Amazon basin are already suffering from the effects of mercury poisoning.

Embrapa says that many of the riverside communities in the Pantanal depend on fish. 'We already have a serious public health problem and something should be done.'

The Pantanal has one of the world's largest concentrations of wildlife, including several varieties of alligators and cayman, jaguars, capybara and the jabiru stork. Mercury poisoning, says Vieira, will upset the whole ecosystem. ...

1 Mercury is poisonous or t _ _ _ c .

2 Dangerous levels of mercury have been detected or f _ _ _ d .

3 Contamination is a form of p _ _ _ _ n i n g .

4 If something accumulates somewhere, does it build up there?

5 If something such as an ecosystem is upset, is it disrupted?

Meltdown

nuclear energy
nuclear power
radiation
radioactive
radioactivity
meltdown

Nuclear energy or **nuclear power** is produced using the heat generated by splitting the nuclei of the atoms of certain elements.

If the reaction in the heat-producing core of a nuclear power station goes out of control, there is **meltdown**, causing **radioactive** material to release **radiation** into the environment in the form of **radioactivity**.

Of all energy sources, nuclear power is the most controversial and the most likely to arouse opposition.

The incident happened when nitric acid was being added to a stainless steel tank of uranium. Victor Michailov, Russian minister of nuclear energy, told Greenpeace that radiation readings in the contaminated area were at least 1,000 times over the maximum permitted annual dosage for nuclear workers.

Hanford's caretakers hope to make the site a model for future clean-ups of radioactive waste and hazardous chemicals.

Another unexpected release of radioactivity from the Sellafield plant was reported yesterday by British Nuclear Fuels.

A Pennsylvania nuclear power station has a potentially disastrous design flaw that makes it and a third of America's plants vulnerable to meltdown, according to engineers who worked at the plant. A combination of problems at Susquehanna electric station could make it impossible to control a nuclear accident. The consultants said that such an accident could lead to a more serious meltdown than at Three Mile Island in 1979.

6 The wrong reaction. Read this review from *The Economist* of a book by Gregori Medvedev called *The Truth about Chernobyl* and answer the questions.

The Truth about Chernobyl

...A series of explosions shook the plant. About 700 tons of graphite and 70 tons of uranium fuel from the core of the reactor, all lethally radioactive, spewed onto the tarmac and the roof of the turbine hall. Another 50 tons of fuel evaporated, releasing 10 times as much radioactivity into the atmosphere as was released at Hiroshima.

Yet so sure of themselves were they, that for 17 hours after the blast, the power station management insisted that the reactor remained intact and that it was only an emergency water tank that had exploded.

1 If something is lethal, can it be fatal?

2 Is it possible to say that a small quantity of something spews somewhere?

3 A blast is an e x _ _ _ _ _ _ n.

It should have been a simple matter to check, but the dosimeters for measuring radioactivity were locked in a safe and the panel in the control room was dead. The managers refused to believe the word of a physicist who inspected the plant, and who was to die of radiation sickness a few days later. Instead, they relied on machines which had a maximum reading of one five-thousandth of the dose some were actually receiving. ...

Some workers received lethal doses because the rest of the site was not evacuated. Night fishermen fished at the outflow to the power station until morning, by which time they were dizzy, vomiting constantly, and their skin had acquired a nut-brown nuclear tan.

There was no evacuation from the company town of Pripyat, where 50,000 people lived, for 36 hours. A man in Pripyat sunbathed on his balcony throughout the next day. Later that evening, he was taken to hospital, vomiting uncontrollably. ...

4 Which four-letter word later in this paragraph is 'dosimeter' related to?

physicist *129* ⇓

5 If a place is evacuated, it is
e m p _ _ _ _ d of people.

Environmental destruction

natural resources

exploit
exploitation

deplete
depletion

The earth's **natural resources** are its land, minerals, and energy sources, especially ones **exploited**, or used, by people in a process of **exploitation**.

When quantities of resources decline through exploitation, commentators say that they are being **depleted** in a process of **depletion**.

Mr Yeltsin's government wants Finnish companies to help Russians exploit their own natural resources.

Crows and Hopis complained that the agency had obstructed exploitation of their coal resources.

We now speak about environmental ethics because we have been made aware of the speed with which we are depleting the world's natural resources and polluting the earth.

Western-style development has brought the Third World accelerated depletion of natural resources such as forests and minerals; the importing of inappropriate Western technologies to replace more ecologically sound systems of agriculture, fisheries and animal husbandry; and the transfer to the Third World of polluting industries, unsafe products and toxic wastes.

damage	When the environment is negatively affected, it is **damaged** or **degraded**.
degrade	When the **damage** or **degradation** is severe, the
degradation	environment is described as having been **devastated** or
	destroyed in a process of **devastation** or **destruction**.
devastate	
devastation	
destroy	
destruction	

Much more <u>damage</u> is caused to the environment in making a car than it causes during its life.

It's easy to feel glum about the world. A billion people are still poor, the earth's population is doubling, the environment is being <u>damaged</u>.

Industrialisation and environmental <u>degradation</u> seem to go hand in hand.

The very success of tourism has <u>degraded</u> the natural environment. Some of the trails in America's national parks are so heavily used (on a summer day, the floor of the Yosemite valley sometimes has a greater population density than Manhattan) that they are scarring the countryside.

Progress has often meant the <u>devastation</u> of the environment by modern industry.

Mining has <u>devastated</u> the environment of Saxony.

Our river water was dirty, our seas were polluted and our natural environment was <u>destroyed</u>.

Her protest was a dramatic last stand against a dam building project that has come to symbolise the <u>destruction</u> of Japan's environment in the name of economic development.

7 Exploitation, degradation, or devastation? Which word is missing from all these extracts: exploitation, degradation, or devastation?

of the route. The agreement may also permit the	....	of the large oil and gas reserves said to lie beneath
has more than 100 years of oil left at current rates of	....	, whereas North America only has 10 years and
document urges countries to assert control over the	....	of their genetic resources through national laws
institute will not be on traditional logging, but the	....	of non-traditional forest products, while preserving
profitably from the North Sea, it must focus on the	....	of small reserves as the big wells run dry. The oil
a 'big reserve of graphite'. As to whether mineral	....	would conflict with nature conservation, he replies
intends to open up the Amazon region to economic	....	in a 'sustainable, non-destructive way'. Speaking in

Habitats

habitat
tropical rainforest
deforestation
desertification
erode
erosion

The natural environment of a living thing is its **habitat**.

Tropical rainforest is one key habitat of global importance.

When forests are destroyed, there is **deforestation**. Soils are exposed and **eroded** in a process of **erosion**.

When plants, trees, and crops no longer grow in an area where they once grew, there is **desertification**.

◆ **LANGUAGE NOTE**
Rainforest is also spelled with a hyphen and as two words.
Tropical rainforest is also referred to as **tropical forest** or just **rainforest**.

These apes are confined to fast-vanishing tropical rainforest or woodland habitats.

In 1940, two thirds of Costa Rica was covered by trees. Since then, the country has experienced one of the fastest rates of deforestation in the world. After fifty years of wholesale destruction, less than 20 per cent of the country retains its original forest cover.

Saghalan calculates that the current loss of 150,000 square kilometres of tropical rainforests a year, and the subsequent erosion of their soils, will drain around 50 cubic kilometres of rainwater annually.

Of the redwood, only a single tree survives in the wild. More than 60 per cent of the steeply sloping volcanic island's 122 square kilometres is badly eroded.

Desertification is not a case of irreversible desert advance. Deserts advance and retreat according to rainfall. The Sahara, for instance, has retreated by 40 kilometres in the past four years because the rains have been good.

8 Habitat types. Each of the extracts 1–6 is about a particular habitat. Complete each extract with one of the habitats a–f.

a desert   c steppe   e tundra
b savanna   d tropical forest   f wetland

1 Coastal _____s such as the Camargue in France and Lake Ichkeul in Tunisia, networks of swamps and lagoons, often at the mouths of rivers, are vital for conservation.

2 These trees come from the tropical _____s, broad grasslands scattered thinly with trees and shrubs, which span 20 per cent of the Earth's surface and extend over some 15 to 20 degrees of latitude between the tropics.

3 Vehicle tracks and noise will spread far wider (_____ does not easily heal) driving away the caribou, polar bears and birds.

4 Tropical deforestation was a major threat to the global climate, they said. Now they are not so sure. The _____s may not be releasing as much carbon dioxide as was thought.

5 Changes in the climate of Africa are causing the continent's _____s and drylands to grow faster than expected.

6 In central Spain, there are areas of poor soil and little rain, collectively known as the Spanish _____s.

Flora, fauna, and biodiversity

wildlife
flora
fauna
flora and fauna
fauna and flora

Animals and other things that live in the wild are **wildlife**.

Plants living in a particular area are its **flora**. Animals in a particular area are its **fauna**. These words usually occur in the combination **flora and fauna**. **Fauna and flora** is less frequent.

◆ **LANGUAGE NOTE**

Flora is used as a singular or plural. The form **floras** is used to talk about separate groups of plants. This is rare, however.
Fauna is used as a singular or plural. The form **faunas** is used to talk about separate groups of animals. This is rare, but less rare than **floras**.

Traffic Europe, the organisation that monitors trade in <u>wildlife</u>, is concerned that traders who deal in rare birds are branching out into exotic reptiles and insects.

One of the rewards of the climb is the richness of the <u>flora</u>: 2,000 of France's 4,200 species of flowering plant are found in the park.

They are also a refuge for species whose natural habitats are disappearing. Castle walls can be particularly rich. They have had plenty of time to develop interesting <u>floras</u>.

The local <u>fauna</u> includes wolves and snakes, and a wide range of unpleasant insects.

"THE ENVIRONMENT PEOPLE KNOW WE'RE AN ENDANGERED SPECIES, THE HUNTERS KNOW WE'RE AN ENDANGERED SPECIES — IF ONLY THE LIONS KNEW WE'RE AN ENDANGERED SPECIES."

There are important similarities in the fish, crocodile, lizard and mammal faunas, but amphibians and birds do differ significantly.

…Charles Darwin, whose theory of evolution resulted from studies of the flora and fauna of the Galapagos Islands.

evolution **118** ⇓

The region is made up of five inter-dependent ecosystems that are home to a rich fauna and flora. Buffalo and black rhino inhabit the grasslands and dune forests, and southern Africa's largest populations of crocodile and hippo live in the lake.

species
wipe out a species
breed
breed in captivity
breed in the wild
extinct
extinction
conservation
conservationist
biodiversity

A group of plants or animals whose members have the same characteristics and are able to **breed** with each other is a **species**.

Animals breed **in the wild**; they may also breed or be bred **in captivity**, for example in zoos.

A species may disappear: it may be **wiped out** or become **extinct** in a process of **extinction**.

Work to prevent extinctions and to improve the environment in general is **conservation** and the people doing it are **conservationists**.

The large number and variety of living things in their environment is **biodiversity**.

◆ **LANGUAGE NOTE**
Species is both the singular and the plural form.
Biodiversity is also spelled with a hyphen.

Only small isolated patches of forest are left, and these would not support any more monkeys. Releasing the monkeys could prove disastrous for other species. As well as fruit, the capuchins will eat insects and small mammals. You could save one species but wipe out 40 others.

Hawaii's 20 species of flightless birds are all extinct. They were unable to fly away from rats and other invaders. Indeed, 40% of all Hawaii's birds have disappeared.

…a report showing that hundreds of tree species face extinction due to excess logging. The report by the World Conservation Monitoring Centre lists 304 species so exploited they are considered threatened at a global level.

Here conservationists found wolves successfully breeding in the wild, the first recorded in Germany for 150 years.

Zoologists were critical of the Environment Agency's attempts to breed the ibis, pointing out that the species had never been bred successfully in captivity.

Only by understanding how modern biodiversity has developed can we hope to conserve and manage the ecosystems left to us.

9 Special species. The words in the box are all used to describe species.
Use them to complete the sentences below.

> endangered
>
> rare   alien
>
> native   **species**   exotic
>
> protected   threatened
>
> indigenous

1 Species of which there are only a few
  individuals are _____ .

2 Ones that are in danger of extinction are
  _____ or _____ .

3 Ones that people are not allowed to kill
  are _____ .

4 Ones that come originally from the local
  habitat are _____ or _____ .

5 Ones that come from elsewhere are
  _____ .

6 Unusual species are _____ .

Global warming

greenhouse effect
greenhouse gases

emissions

fossil fuels

global warming
climate change

Most scientists agree
that the earth's
surface is increasing
in temperature as a
result of changing
atmospheric
conditions and refer
to this as **global warming**.

"I CAN REMEMBER WHEN EVERYONE WAS
SKEPTICAL ABOUT THE GREENHOUSE EFFECT."

Many think that this is in part due to releases – **emissions** –   gas *132* ⇓
of gases caused by the burning of **fossil fuels** such as oil
and coal in industry and vehicles. These gases, called
greenhouse gases, act as a blanket and allow less heat to
escape from the earth, causing its temperature to rise. This is
the **greenhouse effect**.

However, **climate change** is a controversial area, as the last
example illustrates.

Most electricity still comes from fossil fuels, and so generates the greenhouse gas, carbon dioxide.

Trees play a vital part in countering the greenhouse effect. Photosynthesis soaks up carbon dioxide from the atmosphere and locks it up in wood while the trees are alive, and in timber after felling. The world's trees contain between 400 and 800 billion tons of carbon.

Global warming observed over the past century has focused attention on manmade greenhouse gases, presumed to be the likely cause. Some researchers, however, have expressed doubt, wondering whether the Sun - our ultimate source of energy - might actually be variable (as stars similar to the Sun are found to be), and thus account for the bulk of the observed climate change. The expressed hope is that future warming due to further greenhouse-gas emissions might therefore not be significant.

ozone layer
ozone hole

chlorofluorocarbons

CFCs

The **ozone layer** in the atmosphere protects the earth from harmful radiation from the sun. Depletion of this layer over the earth's poles has been increasing: these areas of depletion are referred to informally as 'holes' in the ozone layer, or **ozone holes**.

Chlorofluorocarbons or **CFCs**, gases used in aerosols and refrigeration fluids, are thought to be a major cause of damage to the ozone layer.

The Antarctic ozone hole forms each year as the result of chemical reactions in the atmosphere that liberate chlorine from chemicals such as CFCs. Cicerone proposed dumping large quantities of propane into the stratosphere. His models showed that propane could capture the chlorine and turn it into hydrogen chloride, so protecting the ozone layer. But new discoveries in atmospheric chemistry have now cast serious doubt on this proposal.

Saving the ozone layer from attack by chemicals, including chlorofluorocarbons, has become the first big test of environmental diplomacy.

model *21* ⇑

"I SEE THEY PREDICT MELTING OF THE POLAR ICE CAP. WONDER HOW THAT WILL AFFECT US."

10 **Worst–case scenario.** Put the sections of this article from the *New Scientist* into the correct order. (The first section is a and the last is g.)

Looking on the Dark Side of Global Warming

a   ...The following chain of events takes a pessimistic view of what could be in store for a world that carries on as it does today, taking estimates from the ranges agreed by the IPCC (Inter-Governmental Panel on Climate Change) scientists.

b   At the same time a 'plankton multiplier effect' comes into effect as warmer weather makes the upper level of the oceans more stable. Phytoplankton grow more slowly, because they receive less nutrients, which come from deeper water that now reaches the surface layer more rarely.

c   But in this version of the future, the effect is worse. The depleted ozone layer above the Antarctic and Arctic transmits far more ultraviolet–B radiation to the surrounding seas. This weakens the phytoplankton, further depleting the ocean sink for carbon dioxide, which allows more of the gas to build up in the atmosphere.

d   The oceans, one of the two major carbon dioxide sinks, cannot absorb as much carbon dioxide as they once did. Many scientists believed that this happened suddenly at the end of the last ice age, boosting average temperatures in the North Atlantic by as much as 5 degrees C within a century.

e   The world warms at the accelerated rates predicted by the IPCC as concentrations of carbon dioxide and other greenhouse gases go on building up in the atmosphere, without any cuts in emissions. As the oceans warm, they are less able to absorb carbon dioxide from the atmosphere.

f   This is a safe bet: the IPCC report warns of this positive feedback, which arises because carbon dioxide is less soluble in warmer water.

g   This is a major fear, now that ozone depletion has been found to extend into subarctic latitudes in the spring, when phytoplankton bloom. ...

Green movements

environmentally-friendly
environment-friendly

green
  green party
greens
go green
greening

Products and processes that do not damage the environment, or do less damage than others, are described as **environmentally-friendly** or **environment-friendly**.

These things are also described as **green**, and the adjective is used in many contexts relating to concern for the environment: see the exercise.

Political parties whose main concern is the environment are **green parties** and their supporters are **greens**.

If someone **goes green**, they become more environmentally-aware. If something goes green, it is designed to be more environmentally-friendly.

In the same way, people and things are said become more environmentally-aware in a process of **greening**.

The National Institutes for the Environment could undertake social and economic studies to find ways to introduce environmentally-friendly products. They could assess technologies touted as environmentally-friendly, and draw up a green guide for consumers.

technology 4 ⇑

In a move designed to create a more environment-friendly transport system the Dutch government has set aside 25 million guilders to subsidise low-sulphur diesel fuel.

Germany has a strong Green Party which demands that social change based on environmental values be taken seriously.

Even the greenest greens are coming to accept market forces and the value of a growing economy as a help in cleaning up the environment.

Some employers are keen to encourage employees to go green, and switch to smaller cars.

Spain has been slow to react to the 'greening' of the rest of Europe. And the government is ill-equipped to marry industrial growth and environmental protection.

11 Forms of greenery. The words in the box often occur after 'green'. Find combinations that refer to:

1 groups of politically active environmentally-aware people (2 expressions)

2 what these groups are involved in

3 environmental problems and questions

4 environmentally-friendly industrial methods and processes

5 the change in attitudes and methods as people become more environmentally-aware

6 a person's or product's claims to being environmentally-aware or environmentally-friendly

---

movement

revolution   credentials

green

issues   technologies

lobby   politics

Sustainable development

sustainable development
sustainable growth

Long-term economic planning designed not to damage the environment is described as **sustainable development** or **sustainable growth**.

All Western countries are committed to 'sustainable development'. But what on earth does this mean? How can governments think clearly over decades about resource use, energy, transport, energy **139** ⇓ *industry and the environment when they seem unable to see beyond the next currency crisis or political scandal?*

He seems to accept the Bruntland 'sustainable growth' idea, with its perception of the environment as a reservoir to fuel 'growth' and 'development', and environmental protection as important mainly to keep that reservoir full.

12 **Sustainable development?** Read this article from the *New Scientist* about the transfer of technology to the Third World, written just before the 1992 Earth Summit on the environment in Rio de Janeiro, and answer the questions.

technology *4* ⇑

The Hidden Cost of Technology Transfer

Technology got us into this mess, but technology can also get us out of it. ...Almost every delegate at the Earth Summit will make ritual calls for increased technology transfer as a key element in 'turning words into action' to save the planet. British negotiators report that Third World nations regard access to Western environmentally-friendly technologies 'as of almost equal importance to financial resources'.

The ironic result, as one leading Third World green, Anil Agarwal of India's Centre for Science and the Environment points out, is that 'those Western countries who have been the most immoral in environmental terms are now preaching to those who have been most frugal and sparing'.

Environmentalists in New York, their city's neon lights visible from space, presume to devise energy-saving strategies for Africa when New York uses more electricity than the entire 'dark continent' from the Sahara to the Limpopo. The average American contributes twenty times more to the greenhouse effect than the average Indian. Logically, America ought to seek out India's green ways of living, not vice versa.

But life is not so simple, largely because of the desire of Third World nations to take the quick and dirty road to industrialisation that the west followed decades before. For some, this is the world's most pressing environmental challenge.
...

1 If people make ritual calls for something, do they think about the implications of what they are calling for?

2 Does the use of 'preach' here show approval?

3 Do countries that are frugal in their use of resources use a lot of them?

4 If you devise something, do you think it up?

5 If you seek something out, is it easy to find?

6 A pressing challenge is an u _ _ _ _ t one.

Crossword

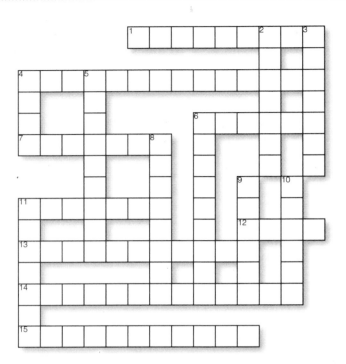

Across

1 These natural ones should not be depleted (9)

4 What pollution can do to wildlife (4,3,7)

6 Pollutants can do this to the environment (6)

7 If you use up natural resources, you _____ them (7)

11 These fumes are dangerous (7)

12 Damage at the top of this chain will have effects at the other end (4)

13 Poison as a verb (11)

14 These issues are green (13)

15 Tropical ones are ecologically vital (11)

Down

2 Everyone agrees this is changing (7)

3 Different habitats have different eco-_____ (7)

4 Animals breed in captivity or in the _____ (4)

5 Student of and carer for the environment (9)

6 Pollutants can do this to the environment when the damage is very bad (9)

8 Usually plural release of gases (8)

9 The greenhouse one causes climate change (6)

10 Warming on a worldwide scale (6)

11 This power or energy is controversial, to say the least (7)

Information technology

Computers, computing, and IT

computer
computing
data
information technology
IT
telecommunications
telecoms

A **computer** is a device for storing, accessing, and processing information, for example by sorting it or doing calculations on it. This is **computing**.

Information handled by computers is **data**. data 17 ⇑

Information technology, or **IT**, covers the technology of computing and, increasingly, **telecommunications**, or **telecoms**, the electronic transmission of information.

Computers are accessible. Far from being the clumsy machines they used to be, computers are now usable, and in most developed countries, affordable.

The history of computing serves only to emphasise that man has invented something very different from a brain: something that is good at precise, fast, encyclopedic memory, sorting and calculation (and perhaps chess), but not at painting, politics or philosophy.

International standards for sending data between computers should enable any manufacturer's equipment to talk to that of any other.

State of the art telecommunications technology makes geographical location irrelevant. state of the art 5 ⇑

America's media, telecoms and computer industries are coming together to form a single business, the bit business.

Technology, especially information technology, is destroying millions of jobs. The hope is that it will create more than it destroys.

The research group sees a growing gulf between individuals who understand information technology and those who are frightened by computers or can't afford to buy them. It also believes that the technology will widen the gap between rich and poor, with rich countries educating people to be IT managers, and poor countries training people to be badly paid keyboard operators.

1 Computer-aided exercise. Match the two parts of these extracts containing 'computer-aided' and 'computer-assisted'.

1 Children look forward to their computer-aided

2 Despite heavy investment, it is becoming increasingly obvious that computer-aided

3 Information networks, computer-assisted

4 Most components for mass manufacturing are first created using computer-aided design (CAD),

5 Preventors and investigators should co-operate, the study suggests. They could be making computer-assisted

6 Several operations are usually necessary before surgeon and patient are happy. In computer-assisted   **surgeon 97 ⇓**

7 When the skier moves her head, the display moves too, making it look to her as though she is on the slope. The ski trainer was developed as part of a sports computer-aided

a instruction project.

b surgery, fewer are needed.   **surgery 97 ⇓**

c learning sessions.

d analyses of crime data, for example, to see where offences are most likely to occur.

e which allows engineers to examine a three-dimensional image on the computer screen from all sides.

f translation is not the most efficient solution. For reasons of context and ambiguity, it is simply impossible to do away with the human touch.

g therapy, robotics and new drugs will increase efficiency and precision. Patients will be less damaged by the treatment they receive.   **therapy 86 ⇓**
          drug 87 ⇓
          treatment 86 ⇓

From supercomputers to palmtops

desktop
laptop
mainframe
minicomputer
notebook
palmtop
personal computer
PC
portable
supercomputer

Supercomputers are very large, powerful computers used for complex mathematical tasks.

Mainframes are also very large, and often used for the central functions of a company, or as the central computer of a university, where they may be accessed by many users simultaneously.

Minicomputers are mid-sized computers that also allow simultaneous access.

The **personal computer** or **PC** originated as the IBM-PC in the early 1980s, and has since become the standard computer for most individual users.

PCs are either **desktops** or **portables**: **laptops** and **notebooks**.

Even smaller computers are **palmtops**.

◆ **LANGUAGE NOTE**
Desktop, laptop, and palmtop are also spelled with hyphens.

The task of finding the shortest distance between points is known as the travelling salesman problem. The number of possible solutions increases factorially: for four points there are 24 feasible routes, but for 30 there are 2.65 times 10^{32}. The previous world best for a proven solution was 3,000 points, which took a Cray supercomputer 18 months to work out.

For all their faults, mainframes are highly efficient data stores: reliable, secure, and no longer prohibitively expensive.

In the 1980s, departments bought their own minicomputers and managers bought their own PCs. These delivered control and flexibility, but buried most of the information where the rest of the company couldn't find it.

The PC has won the desktop wars.

Companies that only make portables will try to convince you that their machines are so powerful that all you need is one big powerful machine and that a separate machine in the office is a waste of money.

Now the books are in the bag; the laptop is under my arm; and I am ready to leave.

The main advantage of using a <u>notebook</u> computer is that you can take all your programs and files with you wherever you go.

A <u>palmtop</u>'s ancestry owes more to the electronic calculator than to the PC. It is certainly the only type that is both light and small enough to fit into a jacket pocket. It is typically 6 inches long, 4 inches wide and about half an inch thick.

2 **Still useful.** Read this article from *The Economist* and answer the questions.

Revenge of the mainframe

...Mr Cray's vision, from the Univac 1604, which he designed in the 1950s, to the Cray 1 supercomputer (1976), was one of centralised computing power and control: a liquid-nitrogen cooled black shrine in the middle of a sealed white room to which supplicants came carrying programs.

Until the 1980s computers were all mainframes, and Mr Cray's were the biggest of the lot. Then came the ubiquitous, ever-cheaper and ever-more-powerful personal computer.

Mr Cray's response was to opt for ever-more exotic technology. He spent $200 million on development without a single sale. Most other mainframe and supercomputer companies have redesigned their machines to find a niche in an increasingly PC-dominated world.

Their approach recognises that the old model of users with dumb terminals submitting programs to be run overnight by data-processing beasts in the basement has gone the way of the punchcard. But the idea of a powerful, reliable machine that can run the payroll, handle sales and churn out bills - all the boring-but-essential work of running a company - still makes sense. ...

1 Are shrines and supplicants usually associated with a) science, b) religion, or c) computing?

2 If something is ubiquitous, is it rare?

3 If you opt for something, do you a) choose it, or b) reject it?

4 If you have a niche in the market, do you have a very large part of the market?

5 Are punchcards still used in computing?

6 Is it possible to churn out something in small numbers?

7 Does the article suggest that mainframes are no longer necessary?

Quantifying information

bit

binary
digital

digitize

byte
kilobyte
megabyte
gigabyte

Computers handle data in the form of **bits**, numbers expressed in ones and zeros. Data in this form is described as **digital** or, less frequently, **binary**.

When information exists in or is transferred into digital form it is **digitized**.

Data is measured in **bytes**. A byte is usually eight bits and can represent one of 256 values, from 00000000 to 11111111.

Roughly speaking, a **kilobyte** is one thousand bytes, a **megabyte** is one million bytes, and a **gigabyte** is one thousand million bytes of data.

◆ **LANGUAGE NOTE**
Digitize is also spelled **digitise** in British English.
Kilobyte is abbreviated as **Kb** or **kb**, **megabtye** as **Mb** or **mb**, and **gigabyte** as **Gb** or **gb**.

"OUR PORTIONS COME IN THREE SIZES:
BIT, BYTE AND MEGABYTE."

Digital bits recorded on magnetic discs or tape are simply zones of a particular magnetic orientation, invisible except to a sensor.

The electrical states of the material are ideal for storing the 1s and 0s of binary code that an electronic computer uses.

A million bytes can capture the text of a 700-page book, but only 50 spoken words, five medium-sized pictures or three seconds of video.

Each frame of digitised video takes up to 1.4 megabytes.

Digitising each fingerprint takes up 600 kilobytes of computer memory.

They predict that disk drives will become at least ten times, and quite possibly 100 times, more capacious over the next decade or two. That would put the equivalent of a good-sized library into the average desktop computer: 800 megabytes to 8 gigabytes of storage, with each megabyte holding roughly the same amount of text as six inches of bookshelf.

3 Bit logic. Match the two parts of these extracts.

1 NEC, the Japanese electronics company, announced last week that it has created a memory chip capable of holding 1 million bits of information.

2 Windows 95 shifts information about inside the computer in 32-bit chunks

3 NASA plans to launch the satellites of the Earth Observing System between 1998 and 2012. They will monitor climatic and environmental factors including cloud cover, snow, sea ice, ocean circulation, and greenhouse gases.

satellite **157** ⇓
environmental **31** ⇑
greenhouse gases **46** ⇑

4 Nextbase uses a 1:625,000 digital map of Britain as the basis of its computerised route-mapping system, Autoroute. The program runs on a standard personal computer, with the geographical data squeezed into 800 kilobytes.

5 Each second of film requires 120 megabytes of memory. *Toy Story* runs for 77 minutes, making the total memory required more than 500,000 megabytes.

6 During the 687-day mapping period, Mars Observer will return 90 gigabytes of data,

a Drawing the full, final version of the film took 800,000 hours on Silicon Graphics computers and Sun Microsystems computers.

b instead of 16-bit chunks.

c more than has been returned by all previous planetary missions put together.

mission **161** ⇓

d The new chip can hold text equivalent to 10 copies of the complete works of Shakespeare or 15 minutes of video.

e The satellites are expected to send as much as 1 trillion bytes of information to ESDIS every day.

f Users enter the start and end of their journey, and the program works out the shortest or theoretically quickest route.

Processors

central processing unit CPU	The **central processing unit** or **CPU** of a computer is a **microprocessor**, based on a **chip** or **microchip**, a small piece of **silicon** with a very large number of electronic circuits on it.
microprocessor	
chip microchip	Silicon and the components made from it are **semiconductors**.
silicon	
semiconductor	

◆ **LANGUAGE NOTE**
Semiconductor is also spelled with a hyphen.

PCs became possible only because <u>chip</u> manufacturers had managed to cram a simple version of a computer's <u>central processing unit</u>, the circuits that did most of the actual computing, on to a single chip. Appropriately, this was called a <u>microprocessor</u>.

Three developments made cheap chips possible: smaller circuits, fewer electronic components per circuit and bigger <u>silicon</u> wafers. <u>Semiconductor</u> engineers are still moving as fast as ever towards further miniaturisation.

Reduced Instruction Set
  Computing
RISC

One type of microprocessor is designed for **RISC**, standing for **Reduced Instruction Set Computing**. This makes for faster processing.

Academics at Stanford and Berkeley suggested simplifying the instructions and saving time on the business of breaking them down: this was <u>reduced instruction set computing (RISC)</u>.

4 The advantages of RISC. The word 'instruction' has been omitted twice and the word 'instructions' three times from this article from *The Economist*. Where do they occur?

RISC Business

Although RISC machines have to use many to perform tasks that their rivals could manage with one, they compensate by executing simple very quickly. Several steps are required to perform an in a microprocessor.

First an code is fetched from the memory. Then the microprocessor deciphers this sequence of 0s and 1s to determine what it is being told to do. Then the results of the operation are stored.

To maintain order within the computer, these operations are performed in strict sequence, synchronised to the ticking of a central clock. Simpler allow the clock to tick faster.

But the biggest gains come from taking advantage of simplicity to reorganise the flow of work through the chip.

Storage

memory
  memory chip
  read-only memory
  ROM
  random access memory
  RAM

hard disk
hard drive

Data and instructions for processing it are held in **memory** on **memory chips**.

Memory is of different kinds such as **read-only memory** or **ROM**, **random access memory** or **RAM**, and others, as explained in the example.

Data can be stored in a variety of ways. The longer term storage on a personal computer is usually magnetic, in the form of a **hard disk** or **hard drive**, but this may change, as the article in the exercise explains.

◆ **LANGUAGE NOTE**
    Disk is also spelled **disc** in British English.

If you want to make the world's most compact computer <u>memory</u>, perhaps the smallest thing you could use to represent a bit of information would be one electron.

electron **140** ⇓

The capacity of <u>memory chips</u> has quadrupled and quadrupled again as the process of etching minute circuits onto silicon has been pushed further and further.

A personal computer contains two principal types of memory: <u>ROM</u> (for read-only memory) which cannot be altered, and <u>RAM</u>, usually in the form of DRAM (for dynamic <u>random access memory</u>) which can be changed but loses all data if power stops.

This is another side-effect of using your PC regularly: the more you work, the more the storage on your <u>hard disk</u> gets distributed across the surface.

Today's densest <u>hard drives</u>, which store tens of billions of bits, pack them about a thousandth of a millimetre apart.

compact disk
CD
CD-ROM

floppy
floppy disk

card

Data may also be stored on removable **compact disks** or **CDs**. A CD which can only be read by a computer, but to which data cannot be written, is a **CD-ROM**, short for 'compact disk read-only memory'.

Small, removable **floppy disks** or **floppies** are also used to store data, especially on PCs.

A **card** contains the circuitry needed for a particular computer function, such as graphics, sound, or even data storage, as the article in the exercise explains.

◆ **LANGUAGE NOTE**
    CD-ROM is also spelled **CD-Rom**.
    Disk is also spelled **disc** in British English.

According to developers, this new technology will make <u>CDs</u>, laser disks and <u>CD-Roms</u> outdated by the end of the decade. The four firms have finally agreed on the standard for this high-density <u>compact disk</u> that can carry 4.7gb of data on its five inches.

If someone comes home from work or school with something interesting on a <u>floppy</u>, ask what it is before you give it hard-disk space on your machine.

<u>Floppy disks</u> have always been cheap to make and relatively easy to copy.

The graphics <u>card</u> on Silicon Graphics' new workstation contains 18 million transistors, which the company claims can perform the equivalent work of hundreds of Pentium chips.

5 **Flash versus disk.** Read this article from the *New Scientist* and complete the table below about the devices described in the article. (The first line of the table has been completed for you. If an item of information is not given in the article, put 'not mentioned' in the table.)

How Flash wins when the Chips are Down

...Conner Peripherals of California supplies 2.5 inch disk drives able to store 120 megabytes of data. In contrast, an Intel flash card with up to 20 megabytes of data is about the same size as four credit cards stacked on top of each other: 86 millimetres long, 54 millimetres wide and just 3 millimetres deep.

...If you compare a flash memory card and a typical 2.5 inch drive, flash wins on a number of fronts. Its specified access time, representing the time it takes to retrieve data, is 250 nanoseconds, against 20 milliseconds. Power consumption is 250 milliwatts as the memory is accessed and 5 milliwatts when on stand-by; the hard disc consumes 3 watts during access and 500 milliwatts while waiting.

The flash card weighs 28 grams, the hard disc 150 grams. And flash can bear shocks of 50G, compared with 5G for the hard disc. ...

Hard discs still have their advantages. The first is that flash can only be erased a limited number of times, although that limit is 100,000 for an Intel flash card. The second, and biggest, is price. A 20-megabyte Intel flash card costs $400 from a short production run of 1,000. ...

One of the most important attributes of flash memory is its ability to retain data without power, known as 'non-volatility'.

Data can also be erased and recorded on flash while it is in a computer or other device, although erasing must be done in blocks of kilobytes, rather than bit-by-bit, as is possible with hard discs or other storage media. ...

	2.5 inch drive	Flash
Capacity	120 megabytes	20 megabytes
Access time		
Power consumption during access		
Power consumption on standby		
Weight		
Resistance to shocks		
Volatile?		
Reprogrammable bit by bit?		

Peripherals

monitor
screen
VDU
visual display unit
keyboard
mouse
printer
scanner
modem
peripherals
hardware

Information is displayed on a **monitor**, **screen,** or, more technically, a **visual display unit** or **VDU**.

Data is usually entered into a computer by typing on a **keyboard**, often in combination with a screen pointing device known as a **mouse**.

Information can be printed on a **printer**.

Text and pictures on paper can be directly fed into a computer using a **scanner**.

A **modem** is a device for connecting a computer via telephone lines to other computers.

These and similar devices are **peripherals**.

The physical machinery of computers: processing and memory devices, and peripherals, are together referred to as **hardware**. (Compare this with 'software' below.)

◆ **LANGUAGE NOTE**
The plural of **mouse** is **mice**.

...the central processor (which can perform a huge number of calculations very quickly) and the 'peripherals' of the computer, such as keyboard, monitor, screen, disc drives and external data links.

Modern airliners use a mix of traditional instruments and computer-generated ones that appear on a VDU screen.

Computers which use an electronic mouse to point at pictures on the screen are easier for the keyboard-shy.

Today, because the personal computer and the laser-printer are mass produced and work using cheap electronic components, anybody can publish text of almost professional quality for a small investment.

He predicts that magazine publishers will soon start worrying about the boom in the sales of desktop publishing software and optical scanners which can copy text and images into DTP documents.

Anybody equipped with a computer, modem and telephone line can send and receive unlimited information around the world almost for free.

The bank spent millions of dollars on new computer hardware, only to find subsequently that only one software program ran on it.

6 Keyboard quirks. The word 'keyboard' has been omitted four times and the word 'keyboards' three times from this *New Scientist* article. Where do they go?

••••••• Qwerty Continuity •••••••

...The standard that was invented in 1872 is known worldwide as QWERTY after the first six letters of the top line of letter keys. The American naturalist Stephen Jay Gould relates that the characters on the QWERTY were deliberately set to be inconvenient, thus ensuring slower typing speeds.

The reason was simple. Typists using the earliest mechanical typewriters could reach such high speeds that the keys were frequently jamming.

Subsequently, as Gould puts it, by some strange 'technological continuity law', the QWERTY survived into the age of electronic, despite the fact that the jamming problem was no longer relevant.

All recent attempts to create a mass market for more efficient, for example the Dvorak, on which typists can achieve touch typing speeds about 40 per cent faster than on QWERTY, were blocked. ...

Software

program
programmer
programming

software
  software developer
  software development
  software engineer
  software engineering

A set of instructions telling a computer what to do is a **program**. People who **program** computers are **programmers**. What they do is **programming**.

Programs are **software**. (Compare this with 'hardware' above.) Programming is often referred to as **software development** or **software engineering** and programmers as **software developers** or **software engineers**.

Friedel does not think that a program running on a single PC will ever be able to reach the level of a good chess grandmaster in tournament play.

Attempts to program a computer to integrate gesture with speech began back in the 1970s at the Massachusetts Institute of Technology Architecture Machine Lab.

When programmers are writing software, they can test how easy it is to use on 'models', programs which make the same mistakes as human operators.

Mr Gates's boyhood pastime was computer programming. Today Microsoft, his company, is the world's most successful supplier of computer software.

India has the software skills and thousands of software developers who are English-speaking and technically proficient.

63

IBM has invested billions in <u>software development</u> but has yet to make headway in high-growth markets for personal computer software, where Microsoft dominates.

Can developers of complex systems avoid using formal specifications and proofs? The question <u>software engineers</u> should be asking about formal methods is not whether to use them, but how best to benefit from them as part of a complete <u>software engineering</u> approach.

language

code
  machine code
  source code

algorithm
object–oriented
file

Programmed instructions are referred to in general as **code**. Programs are usually written in a programming **language** like Fortran or Pascal. This is the **source code**, which is then translated into a form the machine can recognize: **machine code**.

An **algorithm** is a series of logical or mathematical steps represented in a program.

Object-oriented programs consist of ready-made blocks, as the example explains, and make line-by-line programming unnecessary.

Programs and the data they deal with are organized into **files**.

Windows 95 consists of millions more lines of program <u>code</u> than its predecessor, Windows 3.1.

For the machine to be programmed in a standard engineering <u>language</u> like Fortran, the company had to write a piece of software called a Fortran compiler to translate the standard commands of Fortran into the binary '<u>machine code</u>' that actually controls the machine's circuitry.

Illegal in most industrial countries, decompilation turns the strings of noughts and ones that a computer understands back into the English-language statements ('<u>source code</u>') made by the original programmer.

We have achieved such high speeds through very compact coding, and, though I say it myself, some very elegant <u>algorithms</u>.

<u>Object-oriented</u> programming, the latest software fashion, is more ambitious still. It allows 'objects', whether mathematical procedures, chunks of data or video images, to be defined once and then used endlessly.

The full-screen colour picture came from a computer <u>file</u> of 100 kilobytes.

7 Programmed responses. Complete each gap with a different key word or expression from this section.

1 The data is automatically forwarded every 24 hours to a hospital computer, which is _____ to interpret the results and decide whether human health workers should be alerted to a possible problem.

2 Developing a snake-like robot took more than simply stringing a lot of joints together. Most robots, the ones that paint and weld cars or fit computer chips into memory boards, have six joints at most. The computer _____s needed to control them would require massive computer power if extrapolated to 30 joints.

3 The astronomers plan to use a technique known as _____ programming. This arranges the software in modular blocks so that it is easier to modify or upgrade.

astronomer *153* ⇓

4 Mobile information is 'dissolving space and time', he says, citing as an example a company that writes software around the clock, using _____s in different time-zones.

5 Publishers will have to rethink their methods of enforcing copyright because of the ease of copying computer _____s.

6 At midnight on 31 December 1999, thousands of computer systems around the world are in for a shock. Their internal calendars will click from 99 to 00, which their software will interpret as 1900. The 1999 problem is a particular threat to systems written in the 1970s for mainframe computers with the COBOL programming _____, which recognises only two-digit dates.

Operating systems and applications

operating system

command

configure

graphical interface
point-and-click interface

icon

plug-and-play

To function at all, a computer needs an **operating system** program. Some operating systems require users to type in **commands** to tell the computer what they want to do.

Many computers use a **graphical interface** or **point-and-click interface** such as Windows. **Icons** are symbols representing the different peripherals, programs, and files. Functions are activated by selecting a particular icon with the mouse.

Some interfaces allow **plug-and-play**, the possibility of connecting new hardware to the computer without having to adjust or configure the system to take the new hardware into account: the interface program recognises the hardware automatically.

The quality of the operating system determines how useful the computer is. The more effective it is, the more programs it can run at once and the more efficiently it uses the finite resources of the processor.

…Microsoft, the company that gave the world the ubiquitous Windows graphical interface.

Windows popularised the mouse-driven point-and-click interface first seen on the Apple Macintosh.

Files and programs are arranged into icons so that the user can see at a glance what files are available and what programs are running.

PC games required users to enter complicated DOS commands to configure audio, video and graphics cards. The newly claimed 'plug and play' capability for Windows 95 stems from a new collection of Microsoft programs called DirectX that solves the memory problems of previous Windows versions.

application
  killer app
  killer application

database
desktop publishing
DTP
spreadsheet
wordprocessing
wordprocessor

vapourware

Programs for specific tasks are **applications**.

Applications include:

database software allowing information to be stored, added to, sorted, and analysed.

spreadsheets for calculations to be performed on numbers presented in rows and columns, for example in financial forecasting.

wordprocessing on a **wordprocessor** that permits texts to be entered, checked, changed, and printed. **Desktop publishing** or **DTP** takes this one step further by allowing the production of attractive documents of near-professional quality.

Vital applications that have great commercial success are **killer applications** or **killer apps**.

New software that is announced, but that appears late or not at all is, informally, **vapourware**.

◆ **LANGUAGE NOTE**
   Wordprocessing, **wordprocessor**, and **desktop** are also spelled with hyphens.
   Vapourware is spelled **vaporware** in American English.

In the 1980s the firm's applications for its own operating system sold poorly. Lotus, Wordperfect and Borland became the leading suppliers of (respectively) spreadsheets, wordprocessors and database software.

Wedded to his word-processing machines, Wang refused employees' pleas to launch general-purpose personal computers, as arch-rival IBM was doing.

The spread of desktop publishing means many students now work on exactly the same Quark Express software as the professionals.

Most PC users who want a word processor, spreadsheet or database already have one. And there are no new 'killer apps', industry jargon for top-selling programs, on the horizon.

Microsoft has become a world leader in 'vapourware', new software announced long before it is ready for market, then delayed for months as the company eliminates bugs and changes specifications.

8 Counting the cost of programming. Complete this article from *The Economist* using the listed words. (a occurs three times, b once, c twice, and d seven times.)

a code　　　　b programs　　　　c programmers　　　d software

Made to Measure: Cost-Effective Software Engineering

Once upon a time, most software was little more than a few hundred lines of code dreamt up in a computer nerd's spare bedroom; Tim Paterson, who developed the first version of Microsoft's MS-DOS operating-system software, carried its code around in his head.

These days _____(1) is rather more complex. A typical word-processing _____(2) package for a personal computer contains 500,000 lines of _____(3). Transforming Windows into Windows-NT meant writing 1 million lines of new computer _____(4).

Such computer codes are not just written; they are 'engineered'. Developing complex _____(5) is both labour-intensive and time-consuming. A modern PC spreadsheet might take 20 _____(6) two years to develop. ...

As well as paying $10 billion each year for PC _____(7) packages, American companies also spend up to $20 billion on customised _____(8) for everything from payrolls to production lines, with no easy way of knowing whether they are getting value for money. The traditional way of counting cost-effectiveness in _____(9), working out each program's cost per line of code, works when comparing two _____(10) written in the same language.

But try to compare two _____(11) projects written in different languages - there are now over 400 - and the technique falls apart. Source codes (what _____(12) actually write) have to be translated into machine codes (something simple enough for a computer to understand) before anything useful can happen.

A line of _____(13) in a modern 'high-level' language such as 'C' can contain ten or more times as much machine-code meaning as a line of Assembler (which is just one step from machine code). Some of the latest computer languages based on graphical icons are 70 times more powerful than Assembler. ...

Bugs, viruses, and hackers

bug
debug

virus

corrupted

crash

hacker

Software is notorious for **bugs** or errors that cause it to malfunction or even to **crash**: to stop working altogether. Eliminating errors from programs in order to prevent **crashes** and other problems is **debugging**.

bug 89 ⇓

Viruses are intentional errors introduced into programs by people with sinister intentions or a weird sense of humour in order to cause computers to malfunction. Viruses cause strange messages to appear on screen, or data to be lost or **corrupted**: filled with errors.

virus 89 ⇓

Hackers are experts who gain unauthorized access to computer data through a network in order to steal information, for financial gain, or for fun.

Kate Charlesworth

Interactive Computer Viruses

A bug that caused F-16 fighter aircraft to flip upside down whenever they crossed the equator was luckily caught during simulation testing, but similar bugs bring down phone systems, public transport networks and financial markets with alarming regularity.

…a description of the struggles of the early programmers to debug software, is followed by a picture from the notebook of Grace Hopper, developer of the programming language Cobol. 'First actual case of a bug being found,' reads her note, beside a dead moth stuck to the page after being found in a computer.

The system crashed because a programming error had been allocating non-existent tasks to the computer's memory for three weeks.

New computer viruses and logic bombs - programs designed to cause trouble at a particular time or date - are discovered every week, and have often been designed to avoid, or even infect, the antivirus software of most computer owners.

I suspected that the final crash had corrupted vital files in the machine's hard disc.

Law enforcement agencies went on a hunt for hackers in the aftermath of the AT&T system crash of 15 January 1990. On that day more than 70 million phone calls failed. Hackers had been playing in the phone company's switching centres, posing as administrators and gaining access to the computers controlling them.

9 **Matching viruses.** Match the two parts of these extracts about computer viruses.

1 Computer users also have to guard against Trojan Horses.

2 Computer viruses made their debut as weapons of combat during the Gulf War. American spies inserted a new computer chip into a French printer that Iraq had ordered for Baghdad's air defence system.

3 The virus on the hard disc reads the date every day, and on the trigger date, 6 March, it writes garbage, a random sequence of ones and zeros across the disk, obliterating everything that was originally there.

4 Yet another menace is the logic bomb or time bomb, a program that lurks inside a system, waiting for a specific event or time to set it off and do its job. The future dangers are startling.

a Until 6 March next year, computer users are safe from Michelangelo. However, the Jerusalem virus is triggered to wipe any program run on Friday 13 and the Maltese amoeba will strike on 15 March by overwriting the hard disk with garbage.

b A system could be infected with a program that could signal where it is, search for valuable information and send it back to its originator and then move on to another place, copy itself, delete its old form and then disguise itself to fool detection. Furthermore, it could look around the telecommunications network through which it entered the computer for other systems to dive into.

c They are more sophisticated than viruses because they are programs that appear to serve some useful purpose, but which contain another program or virus designed to damage your machine.

d The chip carried a virus in its electronic circuitry that was designed to disable a mainframe computer in its military command centre.

Networks

network local area network LAN	Computers linked together so that they can share information are in a **network**. Computers on a network are **terminals** or **workstations**. If they have no computing power themselves, but depend for this on another computer in the network, they are **dumb terminals**.
client server client–server	The central computer in a network is a **server**. Computers in a network are said to be **clients** in a **client–server** system.
terminal dumb terminal workstation	A network within an organization, for example in a company or on a university campus, is a **local area network** or **LAN**.
stand–alone	A computer not connected to others is a **stand–alone** machine.

◆ **LANGUAGE NOTE**
Workstation is also spelled with a hyphen.
Client-server is also spelled **client/server**.
Stand-alone is also spelled as one word.

...the computer network that supported the World Cup. Spread across the US, the network included more than 1,000 computer workstations with a total storage capacity of more than 2,000 gigabytes, about enough to hold 10,000 copies of the Encyclopedia Britannica.

Aston University has installed a local area network (LAN) linking 2,000 terminals.

Businesses have increasingly turned to client-server systems, in which armies of intelligent server datastores from companies such as Sun, IBM and Hewlett-Packard dish out data and applications to less powerful PC desktops, usually running Microsoft Windows.

When the client software connects, the server provides a listing of the programs available.

The network itself is becoming more important than the hardware at either end of it. In the days of mainframe computers, networks were simply the wires that connected the dumb terminals to the big box in the basement.

The company will merge parts of the system, which will probably be called Windows 97, with Windows NT, designed for use on corporate computer networks rather than stand-alone PCs.

10 The next revolution? Read this article from *The Economist* and answer the questions.

Will Your Next Computer be a Tin Can and A Wire?

For nearly a decade, Sun Microsystems, a Californian computer maker, has mystified its punters with its cryptic slogan: 'The Network is the Computer'. Surely computers are the boxes that do all the work, and the network is just the wires that connect them? Sun's riposte: just wait.

1 'Punter' is an informal word for c l _ _ _ _ t .
2 Are cryptic things easy to understand?
3 Is a riposte a) an answer or b) a question?

Now a growing camp within the computer industry thinks the wait is nearly over, for two reasons. The first is the inexorable rise of the Internet, the open computer network already connecting with some 30m-40m users world-wide; the second is Java, a new kind of program that runs over it.

As well as Sun, firms such as Oracle, a software giant, and Netscape, the darling of the booming Internet-software industry, are spending tens of millions of dollars on a bet that the Internet can do a lot more than pass around data. Along with the computer visionaries such as George Gilder, they think it can also do much of the work of today's computers, holding not just information but software, from word processors to spread-sheets to games and entertainment programs.

Most radically, they go on to argue that this could end the reign of the personal computer. If small, efficient programs can arrive speedily from the Internet, who needs a $2,000 PC on their desk? Perhaps a glorified terminal - just a screen and a processor - would work just as well. ...

Earlier this year, Sun launched Java, a new pro-gramming language (the code in which software is written). Unlike other computer tongues, it is designed to run especially on a network, by using 'applets' (small programs designed for specific jobs). Sun reckons that programs writ-ten in Java could let users do everything (and more) they do on their PC, all from the network. Already there are nearly 400 Java applications, including spreadsheets, word processors and games. ...

4 Does this sort of camp have tents?

5 If something is inexorable, can it be stopped?

6 A bet is a g a m _ _ _ .

7 Do visionaries have a) a sight, b) a vision, or c) a view?

8 Does 'glorified' indicate that the terminal is a) more impressive or b) less impressive than it looks?

9 A tongue in this context is a l _ _ _ _ _ _ _ .

Surfing the Net

Net
  surf the Net
Internet
  surf the Internet

Web
World Wide Web
WWW

e-mail
electronic mail

forum
Internet Relay Chat
IRC
newsgroup

cyberspace

Computers all over the world can communicate via modem and servers through the **Net** or **Internet**.

This allows computer users to send messages to each other via **e-mail** or **electronic mail**. People participating in **forums** or **newsgroups** exchange messages on particular topics by e-mail. People have 'live' audio discussions on **Internet Relay Chat**, or **IRC**.

The **World Wide Web** (**Web** or **WWW** for short) is a graphical interface that provides easy access to information on computers anywhere in the world connected to the Internet.

People looking at information on the Internet, perhaps in a random manner, are informally said to **surf the Internet** or **surf the Net**.

The Internet and the information on it are referred to, especially by journalists, as **cyberspace**.

◆ **LANGUAGE NOTE**
  Net and **Internet** are also spelled **net** and **internet**.
  E-mail and **email** are alternative spellings for **e-mail**.
  World Wide Web is also spelled **Worldwide Web**, **World-Wide Web**,
  world wide web, **worldwide web** and **world-wide web**.

The technology of communication is undergoing revolutionary change. The Internet, a network of computers through which anybody with a computer and a modem can address 30 million other people almost for free, has opened up vast new possibilities.

Almost overnight the development of the Net's World Wide Web changed everything. When I saw how easy it was to use the Web, I realised that a whole new world of communication was opening up.

She analysed records of e-mail at Rand and discovered that more than 10 per cent of e-mail replies arrive within 15 minutes.

Newsgroups are very diverse: they cover everything from the latest stock-market prices to football. If there is a subject area that you are particularly interested in, chances are there will be a newsgroup that caters for it.

...as more and more people build friendships and business contacts in the Internet's discussion forums and on Internet Relay Chat channels.

Some analysts argue that those who spend all day <u>surfing the Internet</u> should pay more than those who just send the occasional e-mail message.

In the US, there is evidence that schoolchildren with access to the Internet are starting to watch less TV and spend more time <u>surfing the Net</u>.

The thing about <u>cyberspace</u> is that everything is the same distance away, no further than your computer screen.

11 **Web words.** Read the extract and match the key words to their definitions.

The web brings together the Internet's vast, disparate resources and makes them accessible using a point-and-click interface. It does this by linking information together using a <u>hypertext</u>-based system, building <u>hyperlinks</u> into Web documents that can transport the user from one piece of information to another at the click of a mouse button. … To use the World Wide Web you need a piece of software called a Web <u>browser</u>, which will be provided by your Internet <u>service provider</u>. The most popular one is Netscape Navigator, which has about 65 per cent of the world market. The browser presents you with a magazine-like screen, on which the <u>web pages</u> are displayed. When you run Netscape for the first time, it will automatically connect you to its own <u>home page</u>. A home page is the first page of any <u>Web site</u> and acts the same as a magazine contents page. From here you can scroll up and down, and you use the hyperlinks embedded in it to 'jump' to other pages. Hyperlinks can be words that are highlighted or maybe a picture on the screen. Click on the link and a new page will be displayed. This may be another page within the same document, or it may be a page at a completely different site: it does not matter where it is as the browser finds it automatically.

browser home page hyperlinks hypertext service provider web pages web site	1 the first screen in a series 2 software allowing Internet users to find what they want 3 screens of information available via the Internet 4 the place where these screens are found 5 an organization that provides access to the Internet 6 a system of highlighted expressions that allows users to go directly to other occurrences of the same expression on other web pages 7 the programmed connections between these expressions

◆ **LANGUAGE NOTE**
Home page is also spelled **homepage**.

The information superhighway

bandwidth

ISDN
Integrated Services
  Digital Network

broadband

interactive

multimedia

information
  superhighway
infobahn

Many users are connected to the Internet by modem and ordinary telephone lines, which have limited **bandwidth**, or capacity. This means that access is very slow, as the example explains. **Integrated Services Digital Networks**, or **ISDNs**, are faster.

A **broadband**, or high-speed, **information superhighway** is where text, sound, pictures, and video, or **multimedia**, will be accessible. The relationship between users and this information will be **interactive**: they will be able to influence and participate in what they see and hear.

The information superhighway is also referred to, less frequently and especially by journalists, as the **infobahn**.

◆ **LANGUAGE NOTE**
   Alternative spellings for **information superhighway** and **infobahn** are **Information Superhighway** and **Infobahn**.

The biggest problem that the Internet has at the moment is its speed. The issue is primarily one of bandwidth, the size of the pipelines that transport data carried by the Internet between clients (individual computer users) and the servers (the Internet computers they are connected to). Most Internet service providers are connected to the Net at a bandwidth of between 64kbps (thousand bits per second) and 2mbps (million bits per second), while most of their customers are connected by a modem running at a top speed of 28.8kbps. One possible interim solution is ISDN, the Integrated Service Digital Network. ISDN can speed information transfer to 128kbps, but this is not cheap.

Kevin is pulled over on the information superhighway

A high-quality video requires a transfer rate of at least 5mbps to work properly. A 60-minute video film would take 24 hours to transfer using today's average 28.8kbps modem. Only high-speed cable, broadband technology has the power to deliver video in real time.

Multimedia enthusiasts dream of a multi-level, interactive multimedia experience, a combination of education and play analogous to a good science museum, with displays of information alongside buttons to press and levers to pull.

Some people argue that the Internet already is the <u>information superhighway</u>; it simply looks different from the television-based version promoted by the cable and telephone companies. Others say that some important features are missing: the real superhighway will combine not just computer networks but all sorts of other communications links, from telephone to wireless and satellite.

satellite *157* ⇓

The Internet is the model many people use for a national or global information infrastructure, or <u>infobahn</u>, or whatever you call it.

12 Superhighway logic. Which key word from this section is missing from all these extracts?

the TV set.) Better still, Oracle's software can deliver	.... programming down any kind of wire, be it a copper
from the software bugs that still plague simple PCs?	.... has come a long way, but it still has a long way to go.
such as Derby and Slough in England. Britain is the	.... laboratory of the world, one of the few countries in
for the Bells' alliance? Opinions differ about what	.... pioneers will want. 'Games, shopping, entertainment
many children. Part of the problem is that the tools for	.... are still being invented. Apple launched quicktime
founded by Bryan McCormick, now a veteran of the	.... scene at the age of 37, expects to find a partner with
chips. The increased power makes notebooks ideal for	.... : a mix of sound, pictures, text, graphics and even

Virtual reality

> virtual reality
> VR
>
> computer-generated

In **virtual reality** or **VR**, people experience objects and surroundings as if they were real. These things are simulated by a computer: they are **computer-generated**.

Imagine a simulation of a car that can be assembled in the computer by a simulation of the production plant, that safety engineers can crash in the computer and customers can test-drive in it. Researchers around the world are developing <u>virtual reality</u> systems that will let designers walk around their products and <u>computer-generated</u> dummies try them out for comfort.

13 **Virtual possibilities.** The words in the box often come after 'virtual reality' or 'VR'. Use them to complete the sentences below. (Each word occurs once.)

	games	programs
environment	**virtual reality / VR**	images
	headset	applications

1 The entertainment industry and the military are already the most important developers of virtual reality _____ , but to prosper, the technology needs to be taken up by the business world.

2 W Industries, which is a market leader in VR _____ , advertised for software engineers with experience in writing games and engineers with a solid understanding of 3-D graphics principles.

3 He sees no danger with simulations of real-life situations, such as driving a car in a VR _____ , but warns that if doctors become able to navigate their way through a brain searching for a tumour, the effects are less predictable.

tumour *101* ⇓

4 A visit to Cluny Abbey can be enjoyed by anyone able to don a virtual reality _____ and experience the stereoscopic images projected by the pair of miniature television screens inside.

5 Virtual reality _____ consist of crude and unconvincing shapes that move in a jerky fashion. Now a British inventor has come up with a device that allows an observer to turn 360 degrees and see a three-dimensional world that has photographic quality.

6 Most companies want virtual reality _____ to run on personal computers or workstations.

Artificial intelligence

artificial intelligence
AI

neural networks
parallel processing

expert system

Artificial intelligence or **AI** specialists attempt to get computers to imitate aspects of human intelligence, such as perception and reasoning.

AI is often based on **parallel processing**, where several processes are carried out at the same time, rather than sequentially. This is a feature of **neural networks**, which reflect the processes of the human brain.

One area of artificial intelligence is **expert systems**, systems that can undertake some of the functions of human experts, such as medical diagnosis.

"IT FIGURES. IF THERE'S ARTIFICIAL INTELLIGENCE, THERE'S BOUND TO BE SOME ARTIFICIAL STUPIDITY."

During a discussion on the problem of meaning in <u>artificial intelligence</u>, the mathematician Stanislaw Ulam once asked what it is that we see when we see. He observed that when we perceive intelligently, we always perceive a function, not just an object. 'We see an object as a key,' he said, 'we see a man in a car as a passenger, we see some sheets of paper as a book. It is the word 'as' that must be mathematically formalised. Until we do that, we will not get very far with the <u>AI</u> problem.'

The latest generation of supercomputers replaces the single central processor with hundreds or thousands of separate processors, all working together. This approach, called 'massively <u>parallel processing</u>', turns the computer into a factory, with thousands of parallel assembly lines churning out calculations and swapping results back and forth.

<u>Neural networks</u> are a special type of computer processor. They mimic natural nerve-nets (of which brains are particularly sophisticated examples) by linking together lots of identical elements. These elements (the equivalent of nerve cells) may be tangible silicon chips.

cell 112 ⇓

The idea of downloading a human lifetime's experience into a machine appeals to computer programmers. In some areas, such as assisting medical diagnosis, <u>expert systems</u> using conventional logic have been successfully designed. But expertise itself is difficult stuff. Often people cannot quantify how they go about things. However, they can, if pushed, usually describe it.

14 Educating Cyc. Read this article from *The Economist* and answer the questions.

Child's Play

'A child of five could understand this; somebody fetch a child of five.' Artificial intelligence researchers are taking a lesson from the Groucho Marx school of problem-solving. To improve on 'expert systems' that know everything about a highly specialised field, some scientists are trying to build an 'amateur system', called Cyc, with the commonsense knowledge that one would expect of a sensible child.

Cyc is being painstakingly built to learn things that seem obvious: that most people have feet, that food is unlikely to be rented, that if you let go of a book in mid-air, it will fall, and so on.

Computers are not created knowing such things; nor do they have a 'childhood' in which to toddle about the world learning them. Yet this ignorance often gives machines a naivety indistinguishable from complete stupidity. How, for example, can a computer plan the simple task of stacking one block on another without knowing the effects of gravity?

Research in artificial intelligence has bumped up against such problems time and again. Although work on the theory of intelligence has produced some notable achievements, it is unlikely to discover the equivalent for intelligence of the laws of motion. To do the sorts of things that people do, a machine must almost certainly know the sorts of things that people know. ...

1 Is commonsense knowledge practical?

2 If you do something painstakingly, do you do it very carefully?

3 Do adults normally toddle?

4 If something is indistinguishable from something else, can you tell them apart?

5 Research has bumped up against these problems: it has
e n c _ _ _ _ _ _ _ e d them.

6 Does the writer say that achievements in AI are notorious?

Crossword

Across

3 The first W of WWW (5)
4 The first page of a series at a web site (4)
7 Enter data using this (8)
9 He or she breaks into computers (6)
10 Communicate with other computers using this (5)
11 The 'reality' in VR is computer-_____ (9)
12 Holds the circuitry for a particular computer function (4)
13 Experience, but not of the real thing (7,7)
15 One type of storage medium (4,5)
18 Where web pages are (4)
22 Short for a type of document production (1,1,1)
23 What computers work with (6,4)
24 Screens of information (5)
25 Access to RAM is this (6)

Down

1 A type of computer and where you put it (7)
2 One type of network covers this locally (4)
3 The last W of WWW (3)
5 There is miniature circuitry on these (10)
6 and 19 Explore the Internet: _____ _____ Net (4, 3)
8 No processing power here, stupid (4,8)
9 What software works on (8)
10 Screen (7)
14 Immediately usable peripherals are plug-_____-play (3)
16 Indispensable application: killer _____ (3)
17 Sort out the problems in a program (5)
19 See 6 down
20 Short for another term for monitor (1,1,1)
21 Symbol on the interface (4)

Medicine and healthcare

medicine
medical
healthcare

Medicine is the treatment of illnesses and injuries. Medicine is also a substance that you take in order to treat an illness, as in the second example. Things relating to medicine are **medical**.

Medicine is also referred to as **healthcare**, especially as a social or political issue.

◆ **LANGUAGE NOTE**
Healthcare is also spelled with a hyphen and as two words.

Medicine is about making us feel better in all kinds of ways, far beyond the rational universe of the health economists.

Making new medicines has been the most consistently profitable business in America for over a decade.

The public love medical research charities which promise us eternal life and which should be getting their money from governments.

The combination of ageing populations and improving technology is forcing governments around the world to review their healthcare arrangements.

1 Medical partners. 'Medical' often comes in front of the words in the box. Find expressions that refer to:

1 the activity of providing medical services (3 expressions)

2 the activity of doing medicine badly (2 expressions)

3 everyone involved in medicine as a job, or sometimes just doctors (2 expressions)

4 what medical experts in general think about a medical issue

5 progress in medicine

6 moral issues in medicine

opinion	practitioners	profession
malpractice		negligence
	medical	
treatment		advances
ethics	practice	care

Illness and disease

suffer sufferer	Someone not in good health is **suffering** from an **ailment** or **illness**. Someone with an illness is a **sufferer**. A **disease** is usually a serious physical illness.
ailment condition disease disorder illness sickness	Other terms for physical and mental medical problems are **condition** and **disorder**. Disease, illness, and **sickness** are also used to talk about **ill health** in general.
fatal	An illness that causes people to die is **fatal**.
ill health	

Illnesses such as cancer and AIDS receive masses of publicity and money for research. Alzheimer's is rarely mentioned, though thousands suffer from it.

I am a chronic sufferer from hay fever and detest gardens.

Last year, British Airways carried 30 million passengers and logged 2,078 'medical occurrences'. The most common ailment is diarrhoea, followed by anxiety, indigestion, faints and sickness. A doctor or nurse responded to 559 of the cases, and flights were diverted 18 times to get a patient to hospital.

According to a report by the Health Education Authority, 12 people die every hour from smoking-related diseases.

She died of suspected Creutzfeldt-Jakob disease (CJD), a rare but invariably fatal brain condition.

...Thomsen's disease, a hereditary disorder in people that causes rigidity in certain muscles when any attempt is made to move.

Explosive technological development after 1940 gave the medical profession enormous powers to fight disease and sickness.

Friends always referred to his ill health, as they did again at his death, rather than to any specific disease.

2 Illness and recovery. Read the extracts and complete the commentary using the key words indicated.

It builds on the extraordinary recent advances in the treatment of cancer. The latest figures show that two thirds of children who <u>contract</u> this terrible illness now <u>recover</u>.

Pessoa is resting at home, having suffered a heart attack two months ago. He is making a good <u>recovery</u>.

The hundreds of other <u>sick</u> and <u>ailing</u> men and women who served in the Gulf wait to see if his treatment will be successful.

There is no easy answer with meningitis. Sufferers become very <u>ill</u> very quickly.

Much of the research involves working with <u>diseased</u> cells

cell *112* ⇓

contract recover recovery ailing ill sick diseased	If you _ _ _ _ _ _ _ _ a disease, you get it. If you _ _ _ _ _ _ _ from an illness, you get better again: you make a _ _ _ _ _ _ _ _ . Someone with an illness is _ _ _ , _ _ _ _ , or less frequently, _ _ _ _ _ _ . Parts of the body that are not functioning normally are _ _ _ _ _ _ _ _ . It is not usual to say that someone is diseased.

Injuries

tissue	The body consists of different types of **tissue**: muscle, bone, organs, and so on.
injure injured injury	An **injury** is damage to the body, for example as the result of taking part in sport, or being involved in an accident or fighting. A person or an object can **injure** someone. Someone with an injury is **injured**.
wound wounded	A **wound** is a cut or hole in the flesh. A person or an object such as a gun or a knife can **wound** someone. Someone with a wound is **wounded**.
heal	When an injury or wound **heals** or is healed by someone or something, the body becomes normal and healthy again.
scar scar tissue	Marks left after a wound has healed are **scars** and consist of **scar tissue**.

The computer presents three-dimensional images that enable doctors to see around the injured muscle, so that the effects of the <u>injury</u> on the surrounding <u>tissue</u> can be evaluated.

In the UK, home accidents kill around 5000 people each year and <u>injure</u> some 3 million.

Three oil workers were <u>injured</u> after a series of explosions on a North Sea rig.

Folk remedies for <u>healing wounds</u> by covering them with mouldy bread or forest fungi may make good scientific sense. Researchers have now demonstrated that moulds and fungi have wound-healing properties.

A car bomb <u>wounded</u> 13 people, including five children.

The Pentagon is very enthusiastic about telemedicine research because it offers the possibility of giving <u>wounded</u> soldiers immediate, expert care.

Mr Simpson bared his left knee to display surgical <u>scars</u> from football injuries.

As well as being ugly, <u>scar tissue</u> is much weaker than ordinary skin.

3 **Self–inflicted injuries.** The words below have been omitted from this *New Scientist* article. Where do they occur? (They occur in the order listed.)

injuries   injured   injuries   wounds   injuries

Teething Problems of a Punch-up

Punching someone in the mouth may do more harm to the thrower of the punch than to the recipient, according to doctors who commonly have to treat such in Australia. Over a period of 20 months, Bruce Hall of the Cairns Base hospital in Queensland treated 102 patients whose hands had been on the teeth of a victim. The were so severe that many required operations and prolonged stays in hospital.

The patients' ages ranged from 13 to 49, and all but two of them were men. Ninety of them required operations and the average stay in hospital was more than six days.

Hall says that impact with the teeth of the victim often damaged joints and surrounding soft tissue. Two patients actually had teeth embedded in their. In seven cases, a hand had to be amputated, and skin grafts were necessary in four cases.

Hall says the patients often waited too long before they sought treatment. These represent a considerable cost to the community, he says.

Diagnosis

syndrome

symptom

chronic

diagnose
diagnosis
diagnostic

A **syndrome** is characterised by a particular set of **symptoms**: exterior signs of illness. Very serious symptoms are **chronic**.

Doctors look at symptoms in order to **diagnose** illnesses: to make a **diagnosis** and identify them. The related adjective is **diagnostic**.

◆ **LANGUAGE NOTE**
The plural of **diagnosis** is **diagnoses**.

He suffers from an extreme case of Attention Deficit Disorder, a recently named psychological <u>syndrome</u> whose <u>symptoms</u> include unusual sensitivity to interruptions. If he is stopped in the middle of anything, he forgets it instantly.

In 1923, when Freud was in his late 60s, he was <u>diagnosed</u> as having cancer of the jaw.

The most common medical <u>diagnosis</u> for <u>chronic</u> tiredness is depression.

Countless sufferers of heart disease could be given more appropriate treatment if only more specialists made use of it. The <u>diagnostic</u> technique is called myocardial perfusion.

4 Not just psychological. Read this article from the *New Scientist* and complete the sentences below. The missing words can all be found in the article.

1 If the cause of a disease is not certain, it is e _ _ _ _ _ e .

2 If you treat something using different methods until you find the right one, you treat it by
   t _ _ _ _ a _ _ e _ _ _ _ .

3 Tiredness is f _ _ _ _ _ _ and extreme tiredness is e _ _ _ _ _ _ _ _ _ .

4 'Syndrome' is sometimes used when the causes of an illness are not understood. The
   phrase 'c _ _ _ _ - _ _ _ ' is used to show this.

5 If someone gets closer to understanding the reasons for something, they h _ _ _ i _ on
   these reasons.

6 Another way of saying, formally, that there are many things of a certain kind is to say that
   there is a p _ _ _ _ _ _ _ of those things.

The Trouble with ME

For the past decade sufferers have fought to get their condition recognised as a biological disease. Now scientific research seems to be backing their claims.

...While numerous theories exist, some with supporting evidence, the cause of chronic fatigue syndrome, more commonly referred to in Britain as myalgic encephalomyelitis (ME) or post-viral fatigue syndrome, remains elusive.

Yet many doctors don't refer to it as a disease; no diagnostic test is available and symptoms are treated by trial and error. That is why the catch-all term 'syndrome' is often used to describe the various symptoms. These include fevers, muscle fatigue and pain, depression and exhaustion. But some scientists believe they are homing in on the causes and effects of the illness.

...There is now a plethora of laboratories in the US working on different aspects of the illness. Combined with research in other countries, such as studies at University College, London that showed less than normal blood flow in the brains of ME sufferers, this surge of interest has conferred some scientific respectability on the syndrome.

laboratory *11* ⇑

The 1980s label of yuppie flu was indicative of the way the disease was then seen: a disorder of the self-absorbed professional middle-class that was primarily psychological in origin. ...

Prescribing treatment

treat
treatment
prescribe
prescribe medicines
prescribe treatment
cure
remedy
prognosis
medication
side-effect

Doctors try to **treat** illnesses by **prescribing medicines** or other **treatment** in order to provide a **cure** or **remedy**. If a doctor makes someone better, they **cure** them and the disease they are suffering from.

The **prognosis** for a disease is an estimate of its likely future course and whether it can be cured.

Taking medicines is also referred to as taking **medication**.

Undesirable effects of medication are **side-effects**.

A system of prescribing medicines by computer is to be tested in doctors' surgeries. The most useful part of a doctor's job is to diagnose illnesses from among a number of vague complaints, and then prescribe treatment

Mr Getty's mother said her son was aware of the risks involved, but wanted the chance to help find a cure for AIDS.

Steffi Graf has to find a way of dealing with a chronic back problem that can be treated but not cured.

In the case of cervical cancer, proven treatments do at least exist. Some tests reveal diseases for which there may be no remedy.

For the 1 in 25,000 boys born with the defect, the prognosis is bleak.   **defect 120** ⇓

The project will evaluate the use of medication to reduce cocaine craving in the early weeks of treatment.

Only 15 per cent of Alzheimer's patients suffered any side effects from the treatment and they were minor: loss of appetite and loss of weight.

therapist
therapy
in therapy

A treatment may be referred to as a **therapy**, but when someone is **in therapy**, they are usually in psychological therapy, as in the last example. A **therapist** is usually a therapist of the mind.

Most adherents of complementary medicine are not prepared to wait for scientific proof. They argue   **proof 24** ⇑
that there is a distinction between a therapy that cures, and one that works by improving response to disease. A cure involves a measurable change in the disease process and this can be objectively confirmed. But a treatment may work, so the patient feels better, for all sorts of reasons.

Choosing a therapist is no longer a straightforward choice: do you opt for a humanistic therapist, an eclectic therapist, a hypnotherapist, a Jungian analyst, a Freudian psychoanalyst, a Kleinian analyst, a family therapist or an experiential therapist? I would say that today, every family in Britain has a member who is, or has been, in therapy.

5 **Treatment logic.** Which key word from this section is missing from all these extracts?

Doctors want the power to order people to take	while they are out of hospital. The mental health
psychiatry at St George's Hospital, London, says that	is effective in controlling some aspects of disorganised
we did not feel there was a need to. Giving mass	to people who do not need it could be irresponsible.
Surely then the question is about efficacy of	in alleviating the sort or mental health problem he
are the best sources of help. However, myths about	still put people off seeking professional help. Only
drugs, which have fewer side-effects than other	, more children will develop problems associated with
Although reasonably fit, Ward will have to remain on	for the rest of his life. The proceeds of his policy

Drugs and vaccines

drug

Medicines are more frequently referred to as **drugs**.

magic bullet

A drug that cures an illness in a spectacular way is sometimes referred to by journalists as a **magic bullet**.

pharmaceuticals

Drugs are also referred to as **pharmaceuticals** when talking about their development and manufacture as a business.

'Even the best psychiatrists make mistakes in their diagnoses and treatment,' he said. 'We can be wrong about prescribing drugs as often as 40 per cent of the time.'

Dr Press reported that in 19 patients for whom conventional drugs had failed, the magic bullet treatment removed all signs of the disease.

Pharmaceuticals is a very profitable business. Unlike many other industries, it is science-driven and, because research projects tend to be long, employment is less affected than in other industries by the short-term ups and downs of the economy.

vaccinate
vaccination
vaccine

immunize
immunization

A **vaccine** is a type of drug that provides resistance against a disease. Children and sometimes adults are **vaccinated** or **immunized** against diseases, for example polio, in a programme of **vaccination** or **immunization**.

◆ **LANGUAGE NOTE**

Immunize and **immunization** are also spelled **immunise** and **immunisation** in British English.

While cholera is still rife, why not vaccinate against it? The answer has been provided by the poor quality of the vaccine available.

Reliable vaccination against the principal cause of bacterial meningitis in this country, meningococcus group B, is awaited, but the pharmaceutical industry is spending millions of pounds on this.

The World Health Organisation has vowed to end polio worldwide by 2000, but several African governments cannot afford the vaccine for national <u>immunisation</u> programmes. Zaire last year <u>immunised</u> 29 per cent of its children against the polio virus, one of the worst rates on the continent, according to WHO.

6 Drug types. The words in the box often come in front of 'drugs'. Find expressions that refer to drugs that:

1 can be obtained without a prescription

2 can only be prescribed by doctors

3 are mind-altering

4 do not occur naturally

5 increase faculties such as memory and intelligence

6 stop people feeling pain, for example during operations

synthetic		prescription
over the counter / OTC	**drugs**	psychotropic
smart		anaesthetic

◆ **LANGUAGE NOTE**
     Anaesthetic is also spelled **anesthetic**.

Now use them to complete the extracts below.

a Selling _____ drugs is very different from selling _____ ones. The OTC market is highly competitive, as most of the drugs have been on the market for years.

b Pharmaceuticals companies reject the idea that '_____ drugs' could be used to enhance healthy people's memory or concentration.

c Almost half their patients are awake during anaesthesia. The problem is caused by deliberate administration of doses of inadequate _____ drugs in the belief that smaller doses will have less adverse effects on the patient.

d Unlike _____ drugs, plants vary in their chemical composition, so processing methods can make all the difference between a safe, effective, high-quality product and one that is not.

e The book also covers the history of the use of _____ drugs, from opium and cannabis to doliuqui, an Aztec hallucinogenic drink from the seeds of the snakeplant.

Micro-organisms 1

micro-organism
microbiologist
microbiology
bacteria
bacteriologist
bacteriology
virologist
virology
virus

The study of **micro-organisms**, very small living things, is **microbiology**, undertaken by **microbiologists**.

The study of **bacteria**, single-cell organisms without a nucleus, is **bacteriology** and specialists in this area are **bacteriologists**.

nucleus *140* ⇓

Viruses are extremely small organisms invisible even under a microscope. Studying them is **virology** and its specialists are **virologists**.

virus *68* ⇑

◆ **LANGUAGE NOTE**

Micro-organism is also spelled as one word.
The singular form of **bacteria** is **bacterium**.

In a league table compiled by the Institute for Scientific Information, the number of papers in biotechnology and <u>microbiology</u> *proliferated from 511 in 1981 to 2373 in 1990 - an increase of 364 per cent.*

biotechnology *125* ⇓

Genetic 'identity tags' that make individual <u>bacteria</u> *glow if they contain certain genes have been developed by a team of American scientists. The tags will give* <u>bacteriologists</u> *an unparalleled chance to study wild* <u>microorganisms</u>.

genetic *106* ⇓
gene *109* ⇓

For many Victorians, the moral implications of developments in <u>bacteriology</u> *were as disturbing as Darwin's theory of evolution had been. The work of* <u>microbiologists</u> *such as Louis Pasteur reduced disease to a matter of chance encounters with germs.*

evolution *118* ⇓

There is no doubt that animal <u>viruses</u> *can jump into humans.*

Public health officials point to infectious diseases that are inexplicably on the rise, such as pneumonia and septicimia in the US. All of this is an argument for retaining diagnostic labs with trained <u>virologists</u> *and microbiologists.*

The model owes as much to evolutionary theory as to <u>virology</u>: *it treats the virus as a multiplying prey, and the immune system as its natural predator.*

bug
germ
microbe
superbug

Bacteria and viruses are also referred to as **bugs**, **germs**, or **microbes**.

bug *68* ⇑

Powerful, drug-resistant ones are referred to, especially by journalists, as **superbugs**.

Most people still insist on using bug-ridden dishcloths, say microbiologists from Arizona University. Their study of dishcloths in 500 homes across the US found 70 per cent carried some sort of pathogen, while one-fifth harboured salmonella and staphylococcus bacteria.

In our haste to kill anything resembling a germ, we have wiped out some of our normal bacteria that serve a purpose.

The virus's makeup has been studied in great detail: it is possible that HIV has been more minutely described than any other microbe that preys on man.

The overuse and misuse of these drugs, he says, has created 'the ultimate drug-eating superbug'.

7 Bacteriological logic. Match the two parts of these extracts.

1 Pasteur convinced a sceptical medical community not only of the micro-organism's existence but of the possibility of vaccinating against it.

2 How does salmonella, a bacterium that attacks the lining of the stomach, affect the joints?

3 Though the Ebola virus may be the world's most vicious virus,

4 Nick Ogden is looking for a bug, Borrelia burgdorferi, which can lurk in the saliva of the ticks that live on sheep. It is the bug which causes Lyme disease.

5 The culprit was a nasty strain of a bacterium, Escherichia coli. This particular germ lives in the bowels of cattle, where in most cases it stays. Last November, however, probably while a batch of cows were being slaughtered at a Californian meat-packing plant, some of the animals' intestines were cut by butchering knives.

6 The Kenyan yellow fever epidemic undoubtedly got out of control because of that regional laboratory's failure to diagnose the cause of the outbreak.   **laboratory 11** ⇑

7 In the end, there are fundamental reasons that argue strongly against the disaster scenario in which some superbug that

a combines the lethalness of Ebola with the rapid air-to-air infectiousness of flu suddenly emerges and wipes out a substantial chunk of the human race.

b For other microbes the labs were even less prepared.

c In 1885, he tried out his rabies vaccine on a nine-year-old boy who had been bitten by a rabid dog.

d Inman believes fragments of protein from the bacteria lodge in the joint.

e Lyme borreliosis, as it is properly called, was first recognised 20 years ago, after an outbreak of arthritis in Lyme, Connecticut.

f the biggest single killer is still the tuberculosis bacillus.

g The E. coli spilled out, mixing with meat that was about to be shipped to fast food restaurants.

Micro-organisms 2

bacterial
bacteriological
viral

strain
  virulent strain

host
parasite

pathogen
pathogenic

The adjectives relating to bacteria are **bacterial** and **bacteriological**, and the adjective relating to virus is **viral**.

Different varieties of a particular type of bacteria or virus are **strains**. A particularly dangerous strain is often described as **virulent**.

A **parasite** is an organism that depends for its existence by living on and feeding off another organism, its **host**. Some parasites cause disease.

Organisms that cause disease are **pathogens** and are described as **pathogenic**.

In hospital intensive care units, the commonest cause of death is a condition called septic shock syndrome, which occurs when the body attacks its own tissues while trying to fight off bacterial infection.

Each year Dutch laboratories post 3,000 packages containing modified bacteria. Given the frequency of breakages reported by the national bacteriological laboratory, this means there could be 15 introductions of modified organisms into the environment in Holland alone.

Hepatitis B is a viral infection usually spread by blood-to-blood contact.

Scientists began to wonder if they were seeing the spread of a newly virulent strain of S. pyogenes. Dennis Stevens and his colleagues analysed strains from 20 patients with severe tissue destruction and other life-threatening symptoms.

We tend to think of such parasites only as pathogens, bringing disease and death to their hosts. But if a parasite is to survive as a species, its host must live long enough for the parasite to reproduce. Well-adapted parasites do little harm to their hosts. We concentrate on the ill-adapted pathogenic minority, which have only recently begun infecting us or our domesticated plants and animals.

8 **Death by sandwich.** Complete this article from *The Times* with the items listed. (a and c occur three times; b and d occur once each.)

a bacteria   b bacteriological   c food poisoning   d pathogenic

Hasty Sandwich Feeds Bacteria's Appetite for Life

The rapid pace of modern life was yesterday cited as a main cause of the rising number of _____(1) cases in Britain. Dr Patrick Wall, of the Public Health Laboratory, said that the rising demand for fast food, especially the lunchtime takeaway sandwich, had greatly increased the breeding ground for _____(2) _____(3). Their effects range from stomach upsets to miscarriages and death. ...

One study by environmental health officers found that 92 out of 113 sandwiches failed to meet one or more of the criteria used to determine _____(4) quality. The _____(5) in some included listeria, salmonella, staphylococcus (which is spread by unwashed hands, open wounds, sneezing and coughing) and Escherichia coli.

Last year there were 82,000 incidents of _____(6) reported to the Public Health Laboratory, a rise of 14,000 on the previous year. Cases have increased five-fold in a decade. About 60 people a year die.

No definitive statistics are gathered on the causes of _____(7), but a study by the Consumer Association's magazine *Which?* last year found that one in six sandwiches surveyed contained _____ (8). ...

environmental *31* ⇑

Epidemics

infect infection infectious	Diseases **transmitted** by contact between people are **infectious**. One person **infects** another to cause an **infection**.
carrier carry	People who infect others but who perhaps do not become ill themselves are **carriers** of a disease. Animals and organisms may also **carry** a disease and transmit it to humans.
transmit	An organism such as an insect that transmits a disease is, formally, a **vector** for that disease.
vector	

The committee also criticised researchers for focusing almost exclusively on molecular studies of the organisms that cause disease while ignoring clinical and health aspects of <u>infectious</u> disease.

A total of 124 cases of <u>infection</u> with the Ebola virus have been detected in south-western Zaire and 89 people have died, the World Health Organisation said yesterday.

The World Health Organisation estimates that 1.7 billion people (a third of the earth's population) are <u>infected</u> with Myobacterium tuberculosis. Most are merely <u>carriers</u>.

Crowds of humans provide new routes for airborne diseases such as tuberculosis, waterborne diseases such as cholera, diseases <u>transmitted</u> by <u>vectors</u>, such as malaria which is <u>carried</u> by the mosquito, and those requiring direct contact, such as HIV.

contagious	Highly infectious diseases are **contagious**.
outbreak	When several new cases of an infectious disease occur at once in the same place there is an **outbreak** of the disease.
epidemic pandemic	When large numbers of people are infected there is an **epidemic** and when a disease is very widespread, there is a **pandemic**.

An <u>outbreak</u> of TB at a social club in Liverpool resulted in seven adults and one child becoming infected. Four hundred people had to be called in for tests. In a parallel incident in the US, one man with a highly <u>contagious</u> form of pulmonary TB infected 41 others in a Minneapolis bar and 14 became seriously ill.

During the eighteenth and nineteenth centuries, there were about eight influenza <u>epidemics</u>; during the winter 1889-90 it is estimated that more than 10 million people died worldwide. The worst flu <u>pandemic</u> on record was that caused by the infamous Spanish flu which killed 20 million people worldwide and led to widespread panic.

9 The plague is not coming. Read this article from *The Times* and answer the questions.

Misplaced fears

Forget exotic organisms, it's home-grown bacteria we must fear

...Books such as *The Coming Plague* and *The Hot Zone*, which describe a world threatened by pestilences of biblical proportions, have fuelled fears of a biological catastrophe. But scientists in the Public Health Laboratory in north London believe that, while it is important to remain alert to biological invaders, the public concern about them is misplaced and dangerously so.

Old diseases have not resurfaced. They never went away. The widespread belief that infectious disease was defeated by a combination of antibiotics and vaccines is mistaken and encourages complacency about the bugs that pose a more serious threat to our health.

A traveller infected with Ebola virus arriving in Britain undetected could cause a local outbreak of the devastating disease, but the virus could not become established in Britain. It is thought to be transmitted by rodent fleas and can survive only in tropical areas where hygiene is poor and rat populations large.

However, the life-threatening bacterium Clostridium difficile is already well-established here. More than 2000 cases of infection with the organism, which is home-grown, were recorded last year. One hospital in Manchester reported 175 cases with at least 17 deaths. Yet there were no government health warnings and no planes disinfected at the airport. ...

1 Is 'pestilence' an informal word for disease?

2 If concern is misplaced, is it justified?

3 If something resurfaces, it becomes <u>n o t i _ _ _ _ _ _</u> again.

4 Do complacent people pay attention to risks?

5 Rats are a type of <u>r o _ _ _ _</u> .

6 If something is home-grown, is it grown in the home?

Antibiotics

antibiotic
antibiotics
penicillin
sulphonamides

Antibiotics are substances obtained from micro-organisms such as fungi designed to fight other micro-organisms, such as bacteria. Substances like this are **antibiotic**.

Among the first antibiotics were **sulphonamides** and **penicillin**.

◆ **LANGUAGE NOTE**

Sulphonamides is spelled **sulfonamides** in American English.

94

Most people associate the name of Alexander Fleming with the discovery of the <u>antibiotic</u> activity of <u>penicillin</u> produced by a mould.

discovery *28* ⇑

Until <u>sulphonamides</u> and penicillin were widely manufactured in the 1940s, doctors could only watch as children died of meningitis and women of streptococcal infections after childbirth. <u>Antibiotics</u> gave doctors 'magic bullets' with which to fight infections. Sulphonamides alone are reckoned to have saved millions of lives.

10 **To be consumed in moderation.** Put the sections of this report from the *New Scientist* into the correct order. (The first paragraph is a and the last is f.)

Superbug Epidemic Sweeps Japan

a An alarming epidemic of infectious disease is raging in Japanese hospitals because some doctors are overprescribing antibiotics. The Ministry of Health and Welfare has revealed that in one hospital alone no fewer than 80 patients had died from bacterial infection over a six-month period.

b MRSA was found in 90 per cent of 590 large hospitals surveyed last July, and in 62 per cent of cases the bacteria were resistant to methicillin. At 26 of the hospitals, 90 per cent of all S. aureus were methicillin-resistant. This compares with an average of 15 per cent in the US and Europe.

c The culprit is the bacterium Staphylococcus aureus, which commonly attacks weakened patients recovering from surgery. It can usually be controlled with antibiotics such as methicillin, but overuse of the drug has produced a mutant strain known as methicillin-resistant S. aureus.

mutant *118* ⇓

d While drugs companies offer doctors generous discounts of up to 24 per cent, the doctor is reimbursed by the ministry at the official price. The more drugs a doctor sells, the higher his or her profit margin.

e The main reason for the upsurge in resistant bacteria, or 'superbugs' is that antibiotics are heavily overprescribed in Japanese hospitals, thanks largely to the drug pricing system. The health ministry sets official prices for drugs but when real prices drop for commonly used drugs, the official prices rarely change in step.

f Japan is the world's second largest pharmaceuticals market after the US, but consumption of prescription drugs is 40 per cent higher in Japan than in the US. ...

The immune system

immune
  immune system
immunity
immunodeficiency
immunologist
immunology

antibody

Immunity is the ability of the body to resist infection. Someone who, if exposed to a particular infection, does not become ill is **immune** to it. The body system that regulates resistance to infection is the **immune system**.

People whose immune systems are not effective in resisting disease suffer from **immunodeficiency**.

Scientists who study this area, **immunology**, are **immunologists**.

People immune to a particular infection often produce **antibodies**, whose function is to fight off the infection.

◆ **LANGUAGE NOTE**
  Immunodeficiency is also spelled with a hyphen.

Native Americans had no <u>immunity</u> to the imported diseases. Why the lack of immunity? And why had native Americans no deadly diseases to infect Europeans with in return?

The levels of <u>antibodies</u> against Vibrio which the new vaccine stimulates are similar to those in people who have become naturally <u>immune</u> to the disease.

Some cells in the <u>immune system</u>, rather than producing antibodies to attack the invader, go after the enemy themselves.   **cell 112** ⇓

Carol was diagnosed as suffering from severe combined <u>immunodeficiency</u>, a rare genetic flaw in which the body's main defence against infection is not properly formed.   **genetic 106** ⇓

Weiner's controversial therapy for autoimmune diseases is designed to exploit something most of us take for granted: the fact that our immune system does not normally attack the proteins we eat as food even though they are entirely foreign to our bodies. <u>Immunologists</u> call it 'oral tolerance'. In autoimmune diseases, some of the body's own proteins are attacked by the immune system.

In the past ten years, <u>immunology</u> has been one of the fastest growing and most exciting areas in biology.

11 **HIV at work.** Read this article from *The Economist* about AIDS (Acquired Immunodeficiency Syndrome) and answer the questions.

The Cause of AIDS

...The immune system, the organ assaulted by HIV (human immunodeficiency virus), is one of the most complicated in the body. Unlike most organs, it is not confined to a single place - the

1 If something is assaulted, it is
  a t t _ _ _ e d.

infections it has to deal with can, after all, develop anywhere. Its cells, known as lymphocytes, grow and mature in bone marrow, and in a gland known as the thymus.

They then spend their time commuting via the bloodstream between various depots, such as the lymph nodes, that are scattered round the body. This ubiquity makes the immune system easy to overlook. But it is a big organ. Its cells, collectively, weigh as much as the brain or the liver, and represent an enormous physiological investment.

Such a huge mass of tissue is bound to attract parasites. Viruses, such as HIV, are the largest class of parasite around. Being little more than gift-wrapped genes, they are incapable of reproducing themselves without a serious amount of help. The help is provided (involuntarily) by cells in the body of the creature that the virus invaded.

Viruses are usually specialists, and HIV specialises in a type of lymphocyte known as a helper T-cell. The role of helper T-cells is to encourage the front line of the body's defence system, such as the cells that make antibodies and the cells that help control bacterial and fungal infections, to respond.

Take these defences away and the immune system collapses. Infectious diseases that the body would normally shrug off become lethal, and the patient has Aids. ...

2 Which noun in the second paragraph refers to the same idea as 'not confined to a single place'?

3 Are things such as cells normally said to 'commute'?

4 Is the immune system normally viewed as an organ?

5 Do HIV viruses reproduce by themselves?

gene *109* ⇓

6 Does HIV specialise in
a) attacking, b) defending, or
c) helping T-cells?

7 Is the front line of a defence system directly concerned with attackers?

8 If someone shrugs off an infection, do they fall ill?

Surgery

surgeon

surgery
  keyhole surgery
surgical

operate
operation

incision

Surgery is the treatment of disease in an **operation** where cuts or **incisions** are made in the patient's body in order to repair or remove defective body parts. In **keyhole surgery**, these incisions are quite small, as the example explains.

Things relating to surgery are **surgical**.

A **surgeon** is a doctor trained to **operate** on people in order to carry out surgery.

'Will it mean an operation, doctor?' asks the nervous patient, expecting the surgeon to say yes only if surgery is absolutely essential. Yet in practice, a surgeon's decision to operate is almost always a matter of opinion; only rarely is there no alternative treatment (including doing nothing at all).

By the end of the century, open surgical operations will be outnumbered by keyhole procedures in most specialities. Minimal access technique more than halves the time spent in hospital, reduces rehabilitation periods, gives less pain and prevents big surgical wounds and scars. In keyhole surgery, a one-inch incision is made and the surgeon manipulates instruments inside the body through this porthole.

When surgeons use micro robots…

12 Surgical combinations. Match the two parts of these extracts.

1 There is now an alternative to invasive surgery: a treatment called ultrasound.

2 Whether people should be able to change their appearance with cosmetic surgery

3 Two doctors performed emergency surgery using a coathanger,

4 Renewed calls for a ban on boxing followed the collapse of the challenger after a world-title fight in London.

5 The couple lodged a complaint in a court

6 It now takes eight days to prepare, perform and look after a patient undergoing open-heart surgery.

a He was rushed to hospital for emergency brain surgery.

b A beam of intense noise is directed at the kidney stones, breaking them up.

c to find their ideas of beauty is a different question.

d cutlery and a bottle of brandy after a woman collapsed on a flight from Hong Kong to London.

e That time could be halved in the not-too-distant future.

f after learning that doctors had removed their dead son's eyes for use in transplant surgery.

Transplants

organ
transplant
transplantation

donate
donor
recipient

reject
rejection

When **organs** such as the heart or kidneys are taken from a person's body and given to someone else, they are **transplanted**. The organs and the operations to transfer them are **transplants** or **transplantations**.

Someone who agrees to **donate** an organ is a **donor**; the person receiving it is a **recipient**.

If a transplant organ is **rejected** by the recipient's body, the immune system recognises it as 'different' and attacks it. Organ **rejection** is one of the main problems in transplantation.

Surgeons in the US have carried out five kidney transplants using a technique that they hope will make more donor organs available. The surgeons used keyhole surgery to remove the kidneys from live donors.

It is now possible to transplant organs from animals into people.

A shortage of donated whole livers for transplantation has led medical researchers to experiment instead with injecting liver cells.

cell *112* ⇓

Ways of preventing the immune system from rejecting tissue transplants are being tested by American researchers. Their goal is to turn off the recipient's immune response.

A new drug that can halve the risk of rejection in the early months after a kidney transplant is about to be licensed in Britain.

13 **Involuntary donors.** Read the extract below from *The Economist*. Which of .
these statements are true?

1 Baboons breed slowly.

2 Baboons are relatively virus-free.

3 Breeding totally virus-free baboons would be easy.

4 The two uses of baboon tissue referred to in the third paragraph are both discussed in the
   extract.

5 Baboons are not affected by HIV.

6 Using baboon bone marrow might be a way of treating AIDS patients.

7 Everyone agrees that the time for this experiment has come.

8 Transplanting animal organs into humans is called xenotransplantation.

Of Simians, Swine and Viruses

...The risks are different for transplants from different species. The
transplant surgeons have their eyes on two in particular: monkeys and
pigs. The simian most likely to become an involuntary organ donor is
the baboon.

Baboons carry many viruses, and more are being discovered all the
time. Their close relationship to humans (one of the things that makes
them attractive as donors) increases the chances that their diseases
can live in human tissues. And baboons are social animals that breed
slowly. Any attempt to breed colonies that were free of diseased
baboons would be a lengthy process that would probably fail.

Tissues from baboons have two immediate probable uses. First, in a
desperate attempt to cure AIDS, it has been proposed that bone
marrow might be transplanted into AIDS patients. Such an experiment
is shortly to take place in San Francisco.

The reasoning behind this is that baboons do not seem susceptible to
HIV. Their bone marrow - whence cells for the immune system derive -
could therefore replace the failing immune system of the AIDS patient
with the functioning immune system of a baboon.

This experiment is extremely unlikely to work, at least at present. Even
fans of xenotransplantation agree that it is premature. ...

Cancer

cancer
cancerous

tumour
  benign tumour
  malignant tumour

metastasis
metastasize

carcinogenic

oncologist
oncology

Cancer occurs when body cells multiply in an uncontrolled way, producing abnormal growths called **tumours**. cell 112 ⇓

Cancerous tumours are **malignant**, non-cancerous ones **benign**.

Things such as chemicals that cause cancer are **carcinogenic**.

If cancerous cells spread, specialists say that they **metastasize** to form **metastases** in other parts of the body.

Cancer specialists are **oncologists**; their speciality is **oncology**.

◆ **LANGUAGE NOTE**
Tumour is spelled **tumor** in American English.
The plural form of **metastasis** is **metastases**.
Metastasize is also spelled **metastasise** in British English.

Is there anything that doesn't give you <u>cancer</u>? Now, apparently, scientists are worried that household appliances could have <u>carcinogenic</u> properties because of something to do with magnetic fields.

As well as a diseased heart, there was a <u>tumour</u> on the organ, but they did not know if it was <u>malignant</u> or <u>benign</u>. I was warned that if it turned out to be malignant, they would have to stop the operation, sew me back up and send me home to die. It was benign.

When malignant tumours are removed with keyhole surgery, they are manipulated into a little pouch that is sealed and pulled out. If <u>cancerous</u> cells leak from the bag, they can re-seed the cancer wherever they land.

Radiation levels of household appliances may be reaching carcinogenic levels...

There are fewer than 350 cancer specialists (known as <u>oncologists</u>) in Britain: America has nearly ten times as many per head of population.

Glaxo Wellcome's development resources were tilted to respiratory systems, anti-viral infection, the central nervous system, <u>oncology</u> and cardiovascular care.

Surgery is effective only if the cancer cells have not spread around the body from the original tumour in a process known as <u>metastasis</u>. Once a cancer has <u>metastasised</u>, the prognosis is bleak.

14 Carcinogenic risks. Match the two parts of these extracts.

1 The reports says that cumulative exposure to sunlight, especially in the first two decades of life, is at least as important as accidental sunburn in increasing the risk of skin cancer.

2 'I didn't want to separate from my wife. When she told me she was going to leave, I said, "If you go, it will kill me."

3 Heavy consumption of alcohol is associated with both cirrhosis and cancer of the liver.

4 Off the record, one of the government's own advisers on air pollution will tell you that he has estimated that 3000 deaths a year could be caused by emissions from diesel lorries, cars and buses.   **pollution 34** ⇑ **emissions 46** ⇑

5 A study from the National Institute of Environmental Health examined 220 children under the age of 14 who suffered from cancer.

6 A recent study shows that remaining thin does not provide any protection against lung cancer.

a I developed cancer of the kidneys because of the enormous stress.'

b There are also reports of an association between alcohol and cancer of the stomach, colon, rectum, lung and pancreas.

c No cigarette smoker is immune to the danger of cancer of the lung. Over 90 per cent these cancers occur in cigarette smokers, but the thin smoker is almost four times as likely to develop the disease as the fat smoker.

d It found that leukaemia was twice as common among the children of men who had smoked in the year before their children were born.

e 3000 a year sounds a lot, and it is. It's more than the number of people who die from cancer of the kidneys.

f Exposure during childhood appears to increase risk into old age.

Alternative medicine

| alternative medicine |
| complementary medicine |
| |
| alternative therapy |
| complementary therapy |

Treatment of illness by unorthodox means is **alternative medicine** or **complementary medicine**.

These expressions are sometimes used showing disapproval, as the examples indicate.

A particular course of treatment of this kind is an **alternative therapy**. Complementary medicine is also referred to as **complementary therapy**.

Evidence such as this makes Dr Brewin very angry. People in <u>alternative medicine</u> are always claiming that orthodox doctors intervene too much, instead of letting nature do its work. When did someone last go to a homeopath or acupuncturist to be told that they did not need homeopathy or acupuncture?

evidence 17 ⇑

Anyone can claim to be a <u>complementary medicine</u> specialist and treat patients or set up a school or issue self-styled 'training certificates'.

The power of suggestion can go to work, causing a fundamental change in the internal environment of the body. Therefore an <u>alternative therapy</u> with a 10 to 20 per cent success rate may have no intrinsic therapeutic value.

A major study to determine whether <u>complementary therapy</u> can help cancer patients to live longer is to take place at the Hammersmith Hospital, west London.

15 **Catalogue of alternatives.** This table with information on alternative
therapies is based on information in the *Independent on Sunday*. The therapies and
their strengths are correctly matched, but the information on their dangers has
been mixed up. Match the therapies to their dangers.

Therapies	Strengths	Dangers
1 acupuncture	Practised in China for 3,500 years. Used for back pain, arthritis, rheumatism, allergies, anxiety, digestive problems and stress.	a There is no evidence that homeopathic medicines confer immunity, so patients may be given the impression that they are protected from disease when they are not.
2 aromatherapy	Most patients appreciate the oils for their calming effect and the general sense of well-being that they promote. Used for constipation, depressions, digestive problems, insomnia and stress.	b Cases of liver damage have been recorded from the use of Chinese herbal remedies, including two recent deaths.
3 herbal medicine	Origins pre-date recorded history. Used for arthritis, migraine, digestive problems and skin disorders.	c Skin rashes if sensitive to the oils, but largely risk-free.
4 homeopathy	Patients are given minute doses of substances that in large amounts would produce the symptoms from which they are suffering.	d Strokes resulting from damage to the vertebral artery, which runs through the spinal column; dislocated vertebra; damage to nerves.
5 osteopathy	Used to treat lower back and neck pain, tension headaches, sports injuries to muscles or joints.	e Collapsed lung, spinal cord damage, fainting, skin infections, transmission of hepatitis and HIV from non-sterilised needles.

Crossword

Across

4 These tests are used to find out what a patient is suffering from (10)

6 If they work, these are cures (10)

8 Smaller than a bacterium, and not treatable with antibiotics (5)

9 Drugs not found in nature are _____ (9)

10 This is an organ or an operation (10)

12 'They hope it might eventually be possible for people to _____ themselves against certain diseases simply by eating leaves from a vaccine-producing plant.' (9)

13 The T in OTC (3)

18 Donors don't just give their organs, they _____ them (6)

19 Micro-organisms with an unusual plural (8)

20 These tumours are not cancerous (6)

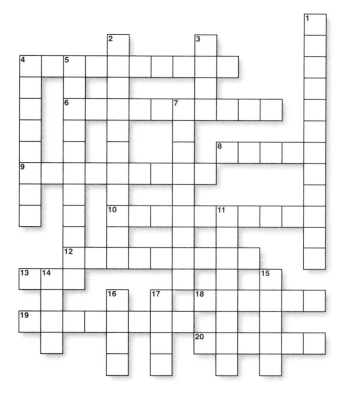

Down

1 The body's defence against attack (6,6)

2 This drug will hopefully make you unconscious right through the operation (11)

3 These effects are not the ones wished for (4)

4 Unhealthy tissue, but not usually people, may be described as _____ (8)

5 Complementary as in medicine (11)

7 Not 20 across, unfortunately (9)

11 This micro-organism causes illness (8)

14 A doctor may _____ a wound, or it may _____ by itself (4)

15 This bullet does not kill people; on the contrary (5)

16 A microbe (4)

17 Ill people are this (4)

Genetics and geneticists

genetics
genetic
genetical
geneticist

heredity

characteristic

Genetics is the study of **heredity**: the way that **characteristics** are transmitted from one generation of living things to the next. The related adjectives are **genetic** and, occasionally, **genetical**.

Specialists in genetics are **geneticists**.

THE ORIGIN OF LIFE

3,562,398,027 YEARS AGO — Two amino acids drift together

6 SECONDS LATER — They drift apart

482,674,115 YEARS LATER — Two amino acids drift together

William Bateson (1861-1926) is one of the most intriguing, if not among the greatest, figures in the recent history of biology. He coined the word <u>genetics</u> and several other useful terms.

Like many <u>geneticists</u>, he studies the fruit-fly, Drosophila, much favoured for research because its short lifespan makes it possible to get through a lot of generations on a single grant.

There is general acknowledgement that the <u>characteristics</u> of an individual are a result of an interaction of genetics and environment. There are well-established methods for estimating the relative contribution of <u>heredity</u>.

There is interest from biomedical scientists who want to preserve the <u>genetic</u> material from as many species as possible in the hope that it will be medically useful in the future.

Lawler was responsible for the study of normal families and of families with inherited abnormalities which provided a solid <u>genetical</u> foundation for his work.

1 Genetic logic. The words in the box often come after 'genetic'.
Find expressions that refer to:

1 the overall genetic composition of an organism

2 a medical condition that is transmitted from parents to children

3 a genetic state that means that someone is more likely to have such a condition

4 analysis of genetic information

5 variation in genetic make-up between individuals

6 influences on someone's characteristics that are inherited, not learned

7 transformations in genetic make-up

disease		make-up
testing	**genetic**	predisposition
changes		diversity
	factors	

Now use these words to complete the extracts below.

a Oncor launched a genetic _____ service for breast cancer that uses computers to interview patients about family cancer history.

b A six-year old boy begins to lose his sight and his sense of balance. Doctors diagnose a rare and fatal genetic _____ of the nervous system, giving the boy just two years to live.   **diagnose 84** ⇑

c The birds of prey are recovering from very small numbers: the Mauritius kestrel was recently reduced to between 10 and 15 birds, the California condor to 27. Can genetic _____ be safeguarded in such tiny populations?

d The editor of *Trends in Genetics* cited a study of how people with a genetic _____ to Huntington's disease reacted to the news that they were at high or low risk of developing the disease.

e With non-identical twins, there was only a five per cent chance that the other sister would develop the disease too. But with identical twins, who have exactly the same genetic _____ , this rose to 56 per cent.

f The evolution of fish into amphibians and amphibians into reptiles and so on must have involved many genetic _____ .

g Researchers at the University of Colorado have concluded that genetic _____ may be responsible for up to 50 per cent of criminal violence.

Nature and nurture

young
offspring

bring up
raise
rear
upbringing

nature versus nurture

environment
environmental
innate

A person's children or an animal's **young** are their **offspring**. Parents **bring up**, **raise**, or **rear** their offspring: they look after them until they are able to look after themselves.

There is debate about whether an individual's characteristics and behaviour are more dependent on genetic inheritance or on the way they are brought up: their **upbringing**.

This debate is often referred to as **nature versus nurture**.

Characteristics influenced by an individual's upbringing are a product of their **environment** and are **environmental**. Those that are due to heredity are **innate**.

environment *31* ⇑
environmental *31* ⇑

◆ **LANGUAGE NOTE**

In this context, **raise** is used mainly in American English.

Sea-horses show sex reversal: the females impregnate the males with eggs and leave them to <u>rear</u> the <u>young</u>.

The practice of rearing unrelated <u>offspring</u> occurs in several ant species.

Adelie penguins <u>raise</u> their young on fiercely defended patches of bare rock, to which they return each year.

A Danish study of the children of criminals adopted into normal homes lends some support to the idea that a criminal's son is more likely to be a criminal than other sons <u>brought up</u> in the same household.

Professor Plomin states that the quantitative measures previously thought to reflect <u>environmental</u> factors should now be recognised in large part to be genetic in origin as well. For example, he claims that in the past psychologists have studied the child as a passive recipient of the <u>environment</u>. The new insight today is that a child can actively create the environment by shaping how his parents respond to him. This, in turn, is influenced by the <u>innate</u> intelligence and personality of the child.

She is in little doubt that the condition has a genetic base and is not caused by <u>upbringing</u>.

Dr Greg Carey, of the Institute of Behavioural Genetics at Colorado University, urged that the 'nature versus nurture' argument should be dismissed. 'The participants at this conference view nature and nurture as complementary components of development, not as mutually exclusive adversaries.'

conference *26* ⇑

2 Innate ideas. Match the sentence parts to form an extract about nature and nurture from *The Economist.* (The parts numbered 1 to 5 are in the correct order.)

1 In one sense, it is plain that criminality is innate:

2 Daly and Wilson have compared the homicide statistics of England and Wales

3 In both cases, the graphs are identical in shape,

4 But it is perverse to ignore the fact that the scales of the two graphs are utterly different:

5 The sexual difference is nature;

a young men in Chicago are 30 times as likely to kill as young men in England and Wales – which has nothing to do with nature and much to do with nurture.

b the national difference is nurture.

c with the young men 30 times as likely as women of all ages to commit homicide.

d men resort to it far more than women.

e with those of Chicago.

Genes and genetic inheritance

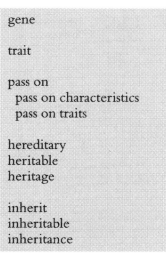

gene

trait

pass on
   pass on characteristics
   pass on traits

hereditary
heritable
heritage

inherit
inheritable
inheritance

Information about an individual's characteristics is transmitted from one generation to the next in **genes**. Genes are the units of this information.

Characteristics are also referred to as **traits**.

Traits that are transmitted or **passed on** by a generation are **hereditary** and are **inherited** by later generations. Traits that can be passed on in this way are **heritable** or **inheritable**.

Inherited characteristics, as well as the theory relating to them, are referred to as genetic **inheritance** or, occasionally, genetic **heritage**.

Until recently geneticists were not interested in particular genes; they were interested in statistics that showed a trait was inheritable. Now they can study the specific genes involved.

The idea that inherited characteristics are passed on in discrete packages is the basis of the genetic theory of inheritance.

Scientists have found the defective gene that causes a rare, heritable disorder, ataxia telangiectasia.

While tallness is evidently a <u>hereditary</u> characteristic, any individual's actual height depends on the interaction between their genes and the environment.

These studies may uncover completely new biological phenomena that have far-reaching consequences not just for human health but for the very way we perceive our genetic <u>heritage</u>.

3 **Genetic arithmetic.** This letter to the *New Scientist* was in response to two book reviews that had appeared earlier. Answer these questions about the letter-writer's attitude.

1 What reason does the writer give for disagreeing with the estimates of genetic closeness given in the articles?

2 What two-word expression does he use to refer to opinions that most people have, but with which he does not agree?

3 Does he approve of the aim of animal liberation groups who want to stop experiments on chimpanzees? What adjective indicates this?

4 What two-word expression does he use to refer to false reasoning involving numbers contained in the articles?

Kissing Cousins

Two recent reviews refer to what is becoming received wisdom - the genetic closeness of humans to chimpanzees. The first talks about the 'minute genetic difference' between us and pygmy chimpanzees, while the second says, 'We share more than 98 per cent of our genes with chimpanzees'.

Similar statements are also used by animal liberation groups to justify the laudable aim of halting experiments on chimpanzees. However, such statements suffer from a number of numerical misapprehensions.

First, the scale on which these statements are made does not have its origin at zero. Could there exist a living object with, say, 1 per cent of its genetic material in common with humans?

Given that all life as we know it is based on exactly the same DNA processes involving exactly the same bases, it is more likely that there is a very large set of common features across both plants and animals without which life would not exist in any form. It would be an interesting exercise to estimate this minimum set. On this scale, I'd be just as impressed to learn that I shared 10 per cent of my genetic material with a tomato. ...

Genes and cells

genetic code

double helix

base
base pair

deoxyribonucleic acid
DNA

amino acid

ribonucleic acid
RNA

Individuals develop following the **genetic code** formed by their genes.

Genes consist of strands of **DNA** molecules: **deoxyribonucleic acid**. The two strands are intertwined spirals forming a **double helix**.

Genetic information is spelled out chemically in an alphabet of four different **bases** made of **amino acids**, as the third example explains. The order of these four bases, arranged in **base pairs**, determines an individual's inherited characteristics.

RNA, or **ribonucleic acid**, serves to interpret and deliver these genetic instructions for cell production.

◆ **LANGUAGE NOTE**
The plural of **helix** is **helixes** or **helices**.

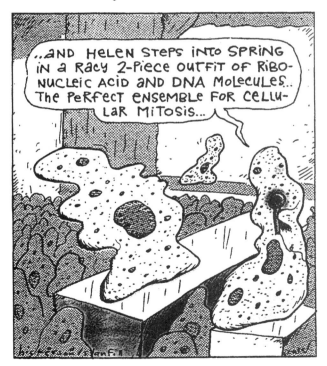

..AND HELEN STEPS INTO SPRING IN A RACY 2-PIECE OUTFIT OF RIBO-NUCLEIC ACID AND DNA MOLECULES.. THE PERFECT ENSEMBLE FOR CELLULAR MITOSIS...

When biologists cracked the genetic code, they found themselves in control of a new language. The DNA that makes up a gene carries a description of another molecule, usually one of the proteins on which the body's chemistry depends.

Each gene consists of millions of base pairs of four amino acids, arranged in the twisting double helix of DNA, the structure that James Watson and Francis Crick discovered at Cambridge University in 1953.

discover *28* ⇑

Each cell contains a message of some 3 billion chemical letters – bases – on its DNA molecules. Or, more strictly, it contains two such messages: one from each parent.

RNA (ribonucleic acid) is closely related to DNA (deoxyribonucleic acid), the double helix molecules that hold the genetic code in almost all modern organisms. Both RNA and DNA have sugar backbones studded with sequences of the four bases which make up the code. In DNA, two complementary strands are wound together, but RNA is a single strand that uses a slightly different sugar.

cell
  cell wall
  cell membrane
cellular
 	
nucleus
 	
cytoplasm
 	
protein
	Cells are the basic units making up plants and animals. Most cells in humans consist of a **nucleus**, surrounded by **cytoplasm**, enclosed in a **cell membrane** or **cell wall**.
	
	The adjective relating to cell is **cellular**.
	
	Cell function depends on different kinds of **proteins**, as the example explains.

nucleus *140* ⇓

◆ **LANGUAGE NOTE**
The plural of **nucleu**s is **nuclei**.

Genes control which proteins are made and it is the proteins that determine the cell's character and behaviour. Red blood cells, for example, are distinguished by their ability to make the oxygen-carrying protein haemoglobin. Other types of cell produce proteins such as the cadherins, which determine the adhesive properties of the cell membrane.

He investigates the way cells transmit messages through the cell wall.

The available evidence goes against electromagnetic fields acting directly to damage cellular DNA, implying that these fields may not be capable of initiating cancer.

evidence *17* ⇑

When a cell makes a protein, it first copies the protein's name onto a molecule related to DNA called RNA. This RNA is a messenger, taking the information out of the nucleus to the parts of the cell where the proteins are made.

Like all genes, the job of these two genes is to carry the recipe for their own proteins. The evidence is that the two proteins work together to control their own production. One of the proteins accumulates in the cytoplasm, the region of the cell outside the nucleus.

4 **The four-letter alphabet.** Complete this article from *The Economist* with the words listed. (a occurs twice, b and c three times each.)

a bases   b DNA   c gene

Finding the True Names

When a geneticist talks of a _____ (1), he means a unit of inheritance. When a molecular biologist talks of a _____ (2), though, he means something else: a piece of _____ (3). A strand of _____ (4) is made up of a long series of subunits, called nucleotides, which each carry one of four different chemical _____ (5), A, T, C and G.

As well as being able to form a chain-like link with the next nucleotide in the line, each nucleotide can also form, by way of its base, looser bonds to a nucleotide facing it; A seeks out T, G has an affinity for C. If two strands of _____ (6) have complementary sequences, an A to the other's T, and so on, then these weak bonds will hold them together in their double helices.

The way to reconcile these two views is to see the _____ (7) as information. The link between the generations is information about what a creature can be; the sequence of _____ (8) stores it. The most important aspect of this information are the names of the creature's proteins, names that are written in As, Ts, Cs and Gs. These are names such as those searched for by the magicians of antiquity, the true names that give power over the named. These true names define the essence and structure of the proteins that do most of the work in the body. ...

The human genome

genome
   human genome
   map the genome
   sequence the genome

junk DNA

The complete set of genes for an organism is its **genome**. Scientists are currently looking at the genetic information in the genomes of many different organisms, including the **human genome**. In identifying the patterns of information in a genome they **map** and **sequence** it.

Only a small proportion of DNA in humans contains genetic code, and the DNA for which scientists have found, as yet, no apparent function is referred to informally as **junk DNA**.

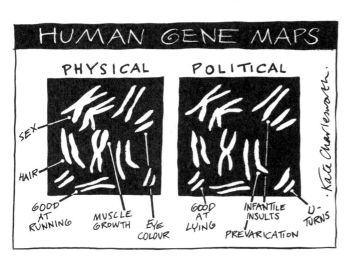

In 1988, a team at Cornell University was the first to map rice's genome - the set of 12 chromosomes which carries all rice's genetic characteristics.

Dr Watson was the first director of the human genome project, which aims to find the sequence of 35 billion pairs of amino acids comprising human DNA.

With international efforts well under way to map and sequence the human genome, biologists are anticipating an avalanche of new information.

The ocean floors were there just to keep the interesting continents apart, rather as junk DNA has often been seen as just a filler between the genes.

113

5 **Not such junk.** Put the sections of this article from the *New Scientist* into the correct order. (The first section is a and the last is f.)

Message In a Genome

a   ...Even though the DNA in a cell's nucleus is often described as a recipe book for making the proteins that build and operate the cell, scientists have known for more than two decades that only a small fraction of the DNA – perhaps only 3 per cent in humans – actually encodes this sort of information. So what is the rest of this stuff cluttering up the book of life, the 97 per cent of the genome that doesn't make proteins?

b   Another 10 per cent or so of the genome consists of telomeres, which cap the ends of chromosomes to prevent erosion, and centromeres, which are attachment sites for the cellular cables that separate chromosomes during cell division.

c   But the debate centres on the still vast, unexplained stretches that serve no known purpose. Many biologists would dismiss around 85 per cent of the genome as simply 'junk DNA'. How could it play a vital role, they argue, when organisms such as bacteria and puffer fish thrive with very little redundant material?

d   Some of it contains the control switches that direct cells to produce, for example, one set of proteins in the brain and another set in the liver. These gene regulators, which turn on the right genes at the right times in the right cells, are mostly scattered throughout the region immediately preceding each gene.

e   These two structures are composed of simple patterns of five or six bases – the letters of the genetic alphabet – repeated thousands of times. 'They play such vital roles in the cell that evolution has apparently provided lots of spares, just in case,' says Robert Moyzis, director of the Center for Human Genome Studies.

f   However, others point to recent research that appears to show language-like patterns in junk DNA which might suggest that it carries an important message. ...

Chromosomes

chromosome
  sex chromosome
  X chromosome
  Y chromosome

Genes are carried on **chromosomes** present in every cell of an organism. In sexual organisms, chromosomes occur in pairs, with one member of each pair coming from each parent. In a normal human body cell there are 22 pairs, plus one matching pair of **X chromosomes** in females, and a non-matching pair of one X and one **Y chromosome** in males, making 23 pairs in each individual. The X and Y chromosomes are **sex chromosomes**.

♦ **LANGUAGE NOTE**
    X chromosome and **Y chromosome** are also spelled with hyphens.

Chromosomes aren't passive storehouses for genes. They have the power to duplicate genes and pass them down the generations. Chromosomes have intrigued scientists since 1882 when the German geneticist Walther Flemming observed their microscopic motions. He found that, in dividing cells, chromosomes duplicate, pair off with their doubles at the cell's centre and then pull away from their partner into the two daughter cells.

The disease is caused by a genetic defect on the X sex chromosome: like haemophilia, it shows up in boys but is carried by girls (who inherit a defective X gene from their mothers).

Chromosomes, packages of genes, come in pairs. In women, the pair that determine sex are both X-chromosomes; in men, one is an X and one a Y. Since everyone gets one of these sex chromosomes from each parent, that means that men must always get their Y from their father and hence their X from their mother. This makes the X gene a good place to look for genes involved in traits that are transmitted through the female side of families.

recombination

When genes from two individuals are mixed in their offspring, there is gene **recombination**, as the example and article in the exercise explain. (Compare this with recombination in genetic engineering below.)

There is an advantage in having children that are genetic mixtures. Sex achieves this in two ways: it combines the genes from both parents and, just as important, it reshuffles the genes in both parents when making eggs and sperm. This is called recombination.

6 **Recombination and evolution.** Read this article from the *New Scientist* and answer the questions.

Sexual versus Asexual Reproduction

...The first living organisms - simple one-celled creatures without much in the way of a social life - reproduced asexually. All other things being equal, a population reproducing in this way should grow twice as fast as a sexual population in which half the members - the males - are unable to give birth directly. Now a team of Canadian biologists has shown that despite the 'cost of males', sex does win out in the struggle for survival.

In the long term, sex should be worthwhile because the recombination of genes between males and females increases the chance that some offspring will have novel traits that allow them to flourish in changing circumstances. But if the first sexual individuals had lower reproductive rates, might they have been wiped out by the sheer numbers of competing asexual types?

Robert Dunbrack and his colleagues decided to test this question in a laboratory experiment. They put individuals of two strains of the red flour beetle into two jars of flour containing low concentrations of the insecticide Malathion.

From one jar, the researchers removed all offspring from each generation and replaced each of them with three adults from a reservoir of the original parent population, which had never been exposed to Malathion. This tripled the strain's reproductive rate but ensured that, like a lineage of asexual carbon copies, it was unable to adapt to the insecticide.

In the other jar, all beetles were allowed to remain in the population and continue to breed. Those whose genetic make-up happened to be best able to cope with the Malathion would presumably leave the most offspring.

1 Does 'All other things being equal' mean that other factors are taken into account in this process?

2 Why are males considered to be a cost?

3 If offspring have novel traits, do their parents have those traits?

4 If something flourishes in particular circumstances, does it do well?

5 Is a particular strain of an organism the same as a species?

6 If something triples, does it treble?

7 A carbon copy is an e _ _ _ t copy.

8 Organisms able to cope the best with certain conditions have a _ _ _ _ t e d the best to them.

Twice a week, Dunbrack and his colleagues shared out the flour between the two jars according to the number of beetles in each - in effect forcing the two strains to compete for the flour.

To begin with, things looked bad for the beetles that were being allowed to evolve. In one experiment, the population fell to as few as 10 individuals, while the nonevolving population grew to nearly 1000.

But after 5 generations (20 weeks), the situation was dramatically reversed. In every experiment, using either strain in the evolving role, the evolving population bounced back and outcompeted the nonevolving population, which was eventually completely eliminated. ...

9 Was the flour shared out in proportion to the number of beetles?

10 Were the initial trends in beetle numbers maintained to the end of the experiment?

11 The evolving population bounced back: it
r _ _ _ _ _ _ _ d quickly.

12 The nonevolving beetles were
w _ _ _ d out.

Replication and mutation

cell division
daughter cell

replicate
self-replicate

replication
self-replication

Cells divide in a process of **cell division** to produce **daughter cells**.

In cell division, DNA makes copies of itself: it **replicates** or **self-replicates**: this process is **replication** or **self-replication**.

replicate *15* ⇑

Chromosomes divide extremely tidily during cell division to produce two daughter cells containing identical sets of chromosomes and identical genetic material.

Most changes in an organism's DNA sequence occur when the DNA is replicated just before cell division.

The simple logic of selection on self-replicating entities remains an immensely powerful explanation for evolution.

DNA replication enables the chromosome to duplicate itself and all the information it carries.

...the concepts of self-organisation, self-assembly and self-replication that come from the biological world.

mutant
mutate
mutation
  random mutation

evolution
evolve

Changes in the genetic material that sometimes occur in DNA replication are **mutations**. Genes **mutate** when this happens and are described as **mutants**.

Organisms that contain mutant cells and new characteristics are also **mutants**. The related adjective is also **mutant**.

Genetic changes occurring by chance in the replication process are **random mutations**.

This has enormous implications for **evolution**, the way that species change or **evolve** over time.

A mutant is the result of small, spontaneous genetic change occurring from one generation to the next, of which physical deformities caused by toxins or radiation are obvious examples.

Genetic abnormalities are more often associated with faults in paternal DNA than in maternal DNA. For example, the cancer, retinoblastoma, is more commonly linked to sperm defects. One explanation could be the large number of cell divisions involved in the formation of sperm; about 380 against 23 involved in egg production. Mutations are most likely to arise during cell division because the repair activity of cells seems to stop during this stage.

cancer *101* ⇑

As mutant p53 genes are found in human cancers, the result adds to evidence that p53 is crucial to tumour growth. Scientists believe that p53 triggers genes to produce proteins which in turn suppress cell growth. When the p53 gene mutates, cells grow out of control.

tumour *101* ⇑

All you need are the three main ingredients of Darwinian evolution: a mechanism for introducing random mutations in a given population; a selection pressure which favours some individuals over others; and an 'amplification' mechanism which encourages the favoured individuals to multiply.

Species evolve through chance mutation and natural selection.

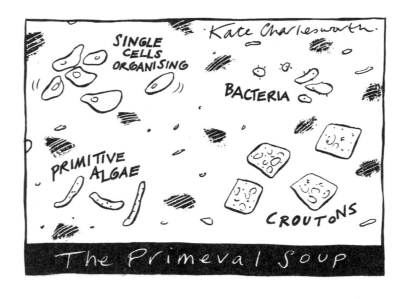

7 Getting the message. Read this extract from *The Language of the Genes* by Steve Jones and find metaphors in it relating to:

1 the liquid out of which the first life forms emerged: what is the play on words here?
2 the beginning of time referred to as a time of day
3 DNA as a set of instructions in the form of a book

Mutation and Evolution

...The first life and the first genes appeared three thousand million years ago as short strings of molecules which could make rough copies of themselves. At a guess, the original molecule in life's first course, the primeval soup, has passed through three thousand million ancestors before ending up in you or me (or in a chimp or an oak tree).

Every one of the billions of different genes which have appeared since then has arisen through the process of mutation. The ancestral message from the dawn of life has grown to an instruction manual containing three thousand million letters coded into DNA.

Everyone has a unique edition of the manual which differs in millions of ways from that of their fellows. All this diversity comes from accumulated errors in copying the inherited message. ...

Screening for disorders

dominant
recessive

An individual inherits a copy of every gene from each parent.

If the gene for a particular characteristic (for example eye colour) inherited from each parent is **dominant**, the characteristic will be dictated by that gene.

If one dominant and one **recessive** gene are inherited, the characteristic will still be dictated by the dominant gene.

However, if two recessive genes for a given characteristic are inherited, the characteristic will correspond to that coded in the recessive genes.

Genetic characteristics include pre-disposition to certain diseases. Recessive genetic diseases will only manifest themselves in an individual if that individual inherits a faulty recessive gene from both parents.

Gopnik and her colleagues published an analysis of language impairment running in a family in London. Most afflicted members of the family have average non-verbal IQs, but speak slowly, frequently missing pronouns and suffixes involved in forming plurals and the past tense. The pattern of inheritance suggests a trait controlled by a single <u>dominant</u> gene.

After demanding a genetic test, Annie's younger brother has found out that he will escape Annie's fate, because he has inherited the faulty gene from only one parent. For <u>recessive</u> disorders such as Friedreich's ataxia to develop, both parents must pass on the faulty gene.

genetic disorder	Genetic diseases, illnesses and conditions with genetic causes, are **genetic disorders**. These causes are referred to as **genetic abnormalities** or **genetic defects**.
genetic abnormality genetic defect	Medical testing to see whether someone carries abnormal genes is **genetic screening**.
genetic screening	

The Marsden Hospital is introducing a 'family history of ovarian cancer' clinic for patients who may be at risk from the disease. There is a small incidence of ovarian cancer associated with <u>genetic abnormalities</u>, and the clinic aims to alert the families concerned and inform them of the need for <u>screening</u>.

Wilson studies mice that have the same <u>genetic defect</u> that causes cystic fibrosis in people.

Cousins have an eighth of their genes in common; if they both carry a recessive gene for some devastating <u>genetic disorder</u>, the chance of the offspring of such a union having a pair of such genes, and so manifesting the disease, are high.

8 Tracking down the culprit. Which expression from this section is missing from all these extracts?

were to appear, these too can be picked up by	....	and corrected by gene therapy. One worrisome
ten years. Professor Sikora also predicted eventual	....	for every individual at age two to identify their cancer
late in melanoma development. As a consequence,	....	for the traits that put people at risk of melanoma
risk. 'But I am afraid that if we allow uncontrolled	....	, employers will just choose people who can stand bad
This opens up the possibility that a simple	....	test could identify people who are at risk of developing
also some serious conferences. One will ask whether	....	is just eugenics through the back door. Another
gender and build of a baby. A quarter opposed	....	altogether. The broad view of the audience was

Gene therapy

gene therapy

germ–line therapy

genetic manipulation

gene pool

Gene therapy attempts to correct genetic defects by inserting a healthy copy of a faulty or missing gene into cells in a patient's body.

In the future, **germ–line therapy** may be used to correct genetic defects by intervening directly on the reproductive cells – sperm and eggs – so that these defects are not passed on to future generations.

These are examples of **genetic manipulation**: altering the genetic make-up of people, animals, and plants not only to cure and prevent disease, but to 'improve' them generally. This expression is often used when discussing the ethics of such activities.

Some people are worried about the effects of this work on the **gene pool**, the range of genetic variety within a particular species.

◆ **LANGUAGE NOTE**
Germ–line is also spelled as one word.

GENETICALLY-ALTERED MICE, CAPABLE OF UNDERSTANDING RUDIMENTARY SIT-COMS

To be useful, therapeutic genes must first be delivered to the tissue where they are needed. Those for   **tissue 82** ⇑
cystic fibrosis, an important target for <u>gene therapy</u>, must be inserted into cells in the lining of the lung.

Others argue that <u>germ-line therapy</u> would have a variety of harmful biological and social consequences, such as reducing the size of the human <u>gene pool</u>, or encouraging a black market in therapy that would make children taller or brighter.

Jeremy Rifkin, enemy of all <u>genetic manipulation</u>, threatened to sue America's National Institutes of Health for testing healthy but short children. He argues that the hazards - possible slight increases in the risks of leukaemia and diabetes - are not justified in 'patients' without a disease.

9 Case studies in gene therapy. Match the two parts of these extracts.

1 Research teams in the US are now exploring the use of gene therapy

2 The spread of cancers in the livers of mice can be dramatically reduced by an
experimental form of gene therapy that makes the tumour cells commit suicide.   **tumour 101** ⇑

3 Dr Valle has a patient with ornithine aminotransferase deficiency, a rare genetic
disorder that causes blindness, usually by the age of 40. The progress of symptoms   **symptom 84** ⇑
can be slowed by limiting the sufferer's protein intake.

4 Hopes are rising that the first form of gene therapy to be given to newborn babies
will be a success.

5 Why should people not use gene therapy to improve their lot in life?

6 DISCOVERIES RAISE HOPE OF GENE THERAPY FOR BALDNESS.

a A Californian team of researchers announced last week that three children who
received experimental therapy for a rare genetic immunodeficiency disease had   **immunodeficiency**
made better progress than expected.   **96** ⇑

b Because this youngster thought that gene therapy for his disease was imminent, he
endangered his eyesight by not sticking to the diet.

c for diseases as disparate as Parkinson's, skin cancer, cystic fibrosis and AIDS.

d Researchers at Bradford University have isolated the cells that regulate hair growth
from a balding scalp.

e Taking a growth gene might be compared with having a face-lift or other cosmetic
surgery.   **surgery 97** ⇑

f The research increases the hope that gene therapy for the disease will work in humans.

Genetic engineering

genetically engineered
genetic engineering

genetically modified
organism
gmo

splice

recombinant DNA
recombination

clone
cloning

Genetic manipulation is referred to more neutrally as **genetic engineering**. Organisms whose cells have been genetically modified have been **genetically engineered**.

An organism altered in this way is a **genetically modified organism** or **gmo**.

DNA segments from one organism may be inserted or **spliced** into the DNA of another, perhaps unrelated, organism to produce genes that do not occur in nature in a process of **recombination**. This is **recombinant DNA** technology. (Compare this with natural recombination above.)

A **clone** is a gene that has been isolated and copied or **cloned** in a process of **cloning**. Clones are also complete organisms that have been produced by manipulating cells from an embryo to produce offspring with the same genetic make-up as each other.

◆ **LANGUAGE NOTE**
   GMO is an alternative spelling for **gmo**.

Genetic engineering opened up tremendous possibilities for developing new plant varieties with built-in defences against pests and diseases. To date, more than 60 plant species have been genetically engineered.   **disease 81** ⇑

If the emerging genetic engineering industry has its way, in the years ahead the world will see massive releases of genetically modified organisms into the environment.

Recombinant DNA techniques can splice a gene from one plant or animal into another. Using these methods, researchers have already produced a range of gmos. There are potatoes with extra genes from bacteria; when fried, the potatoes make crisper chips. There is wheat that is resistant to herbicides, so the fields where it grows can be sprayed with impunity. There are tomatoes made frost-resistant by including genes from cold-water fish.   **bacteria 89** ⇑

For the moment, cloning of human embryos is unlikely to be approved anywhere in the world.

The first gene was cloned - isolated and reproduced on its own in the laboratory - in 1972. At the time, scientists were so worried about the implications of what they were doing that they considered a voluntary moratorium on the recombination of cloned genes into the DNA of other organisms.

Some scientists who work on viruses oppose destruction because there may still be things to learn from studying smallpox. The World Health Organisation says scientists have now produced harmless <u>clones</u> of the virus and have its full genetic blueprint.

virus **89** ⇑

transgenic transgenics	Organisms that have been genetically manipulated and contain genes from other, unrelated organisms, are **transgenic**.

This activity is **transgenics**.

Massachusetts scientists have genetically altered a herd of goats to produce anti-cancer proteins in their milk. The <u>transgenic</u> goats grew from embryos fitted with fragments of human DNA.

In developing countries, farmers may find the price of <u>transgenics</u> just too high. Worse, some could lose critical income as industrialised countries begin to grow genetically engineered crops to replace crops that are at present imported from the South.

10 **Case studies in genetic engineering.** Match the two parts of these extracts.

1 These findings increase fears that weeds will crossbreed with genetically engineered crops,

finding **26** ⇑

2 Plants that could be harvested commercially for the plastic they produce have moved a big step closer.

3 There are obvious benefits to genetically enhanced food,

4 Hammond points out that there is no genetic material in the beer because like most lagers, it is filtered and pasteurised.

5 Researchers tried to thread genes through pores in the plant cell membrane after they had been opened up electrically, a technique called electroporation.

6 Just as worrying for the public is the surgeon-playing-God scenario. The fear that transplant teams armed with genetically engineered animal organs will indulge in reckless experiments on human patients.

surgeon **97** ⇑
transplant **99** ⇑
organ **99** ⇑
experiment **13** ⇑

a Biologists at the Carnegie Institution of Washington have genetically engineered plants that yield a hundred times more plastic than those produced in previous experiments.

b In the past decade, there have been three attempts to transplant baboon organs into human patients, all failing and all generating storms of controversy.

c inheriting traits which make them better able to survive drought, frost or pests.

d such as enhanced taste and longer shelf-life.

e The big brewers remain cautious about exploiting the new technology, however, because they doubt whether consumers want to buy genetically engineered beer.

f The first genetically engineered rice was created using this technique in the late 1980s. Around the same time, biologists invented 'gene guns', devices that shoot the genes directly into plant cells.

Biotechnology

biotech
biotechnologist

biotechnology

Genetic engineering is one of the main areas of **biotech** or **biotechnology**, the practical application of biology and biochemistry. Scientists working in this field are **biotechnologists**.

Biotech and biotechnology are often used when talking about genetic engineering and other biochemical activities as a business.

"YOUR PROBLEM IS IN THE GENE WHICH MAKES ANTIBODIES, BUT SINCE THE BIOPHASE CORP. NOW HAS A PATENT ON THAT GENE, I CAN'T DO ANYTHING FOR YOU."

Using the techniques of recombinant DNA technology, he has genetically engineered a vaccine that is heat stable, easy to produce, easy to administer and cheap. A chance encounter in 1983 with Genentech, the first commercial biotechnology company, was a pivotal moment in the development of the vaccine. **vaccine 87** ⇑

Californian biotechnologist Kary Mullis invented the gene duplication technique called the polymerase chain reaction that allows a piece of DNA to be cloned millions of times in a matter of hours. He has founded a company called Stargene to clone the DNA of famous people.

Although the industry is still losing money overall, several of the leading firms - Chiron, Biogen, Genzyme and Amgen - are making a profit. But in a couple of decades the biotech industry as a whole could be as large as the business of producing conventional drugs. **drug 87** ⇑

11 **Patent arrogance?** Put the sections of this article from the *Independent* into the correct order. (The first section is a and the last is e.)

Is this the Work of Man or Nature?

Tomorrow, a band of technocrats will assess the morality of granting the first European patent on a genetically engineered animal

a Tomorrow, the Book of Genesis will be rewritten. In the unlikely setting of the European Patent Office in Munich, a group of international civil servants will decide whether living animals are part of the natural world or whether they can be artefacts - inventions - created by human ingenuity.

b And it is unlikely to stop there. 'Oncodogs' or 'Oncorabbits' or 'Oncomonkeys' are likely to follow, designed to be used in cancer research.

c At issue is a mouse. Not an ordinary mouse, though. This is the first animal not to have been invented by God, but by humans. In 1984, genetic engineers at Harvard University manipulated the biological instructions encoded in the genes of a laboratory mouse. The engineers, Timothy Stewart, Paul Pattengale and Philip Leder, unzipped the double helix of the mouse's DNA and stitched in a gene that fatally dooms the animal to the development of cancer.

d Now the president and fellows of Harvard University want to patent the animal as their 'invention', because it has, in the language of patent law, 'utility' in research into how tumours form. The university has even coined a trademark for its product, the Harvard Oncomouse, and wants to profit from the exclusive right to sell these animals.

e Patents are immensely important in the global biotechnology industry that has developed over the past 20 years. The industry spends more than $100 million a year just to protect its intellectual property, which of course ranges far more widely than patents on living animals. ...

invention 6 ⇑

cancer 101 ⇑

tumour 101 ⇑

Genetic fingerprinting

genetic fingerprinting

DNA fingerprints

Genetic fingerprinting is the use of genetic techniques to see if people are related, as the example illustrates, or in crime detection, as the article in the exercise explains.

The DNA patterns of individuals are their **DNA fingerprints**.

Corpses that could not be recognised by standard methods after an air crash in February were eventually identified by DNA fingerprints. This is the first time that genetic fingerprinting has been used during a disaster. Within ten days of the crash near Strasbourg, a team of French forensic scientists had identified 68 of the 87 corpses by conventional methods such as dental records. Sixteen of the remaining corpses were identified by comparing their DNA profiles with those of their nearest relatives. The technique relies on detecting familial traits within DNA.

12 Not so sure. Read this article from the *New Scientist* about a report by the American National Academy of Sciences on genetic fingerprinting. Complete it using the words listed. (a occurs twice, b three times, and c four times.)

a data   b DNA   c match

Battle over Genetic Fingerprinting

...The FBI should change the way it calculates the probability that a random person's DNA would match samples found at the scene of a crime, says the report. The new procedures would increase the estimated probability of a chance match from 1 in many millions to 1 in perhaps 10,000.

The committee called for detailed study of 15 to 20 ethnic groups in the US. Two people from the same ethnic group are more likely to have a close _____ (1), yet in court cases, the likelihood of a random _____ (2) between _____ (3) from two different people is usually estimated using _____ (4) from the general population.

Last month, a new analysis of genetic _____ (5) from an isolated indigenous group in South America produced a dramatic illustration of this point. Kenneth Kidd of Yale University collected genetic profiles of a tribe called the Karitiana. Kidd has reported in an article in the journal *Science* that none of the people in this population had identical genetic profiles. A strong supporter of using _____ (6) in the courts, Kidd used this data to show how rare random matches are, even among relatives, and thus how reliable _____ (7) techniques are.

But Kidd's data contained a few surprises for Laurence Mueller, an evolutionary biologist at the University of California. Mueller assumed that Kidd had looked for a _____ (8) at all seven locations, or loci, on the chromosome where he had collected data. Mueller thought there might be some matches if only three or four loci were considered, as is typical in criminal cases. He programmed his computer to compare the 1431 possible combinations of pairs in this population, using the FBI's criteria for a _____ (9).

When the results emerged, Mueller was astonished to find 322 pairs that matched at four loci, 61 matching pairs at five loci, five pairs of Indians that matched at six loci, and two pairs that matched at all seven loci. This is exactly what Kidd had said would not occur. ...

analysis *17* ⇑

article *26* ⇑
journal *26* ⇑

programme *63* ⇑

results *26* ⇑

Crossword

Across

1 These features can be passed on from generation to generation (6)

4 Illnesses and conditions, sometimes genetic in origin (9)

11 The same as 1, but in the singular (14)

14 Not environmental (6)

15 DNA comes in this shape (6,5)

16 When genetic, this gives the instructions for life (4)

17 What animals with genes from other animals are (10)

18 Genetic _____ is genetic manipulation (11)

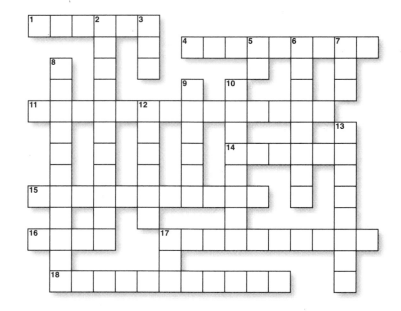

Down

2 Characteristics that can be passed on are this (11)

3 _____ chromosomes: men have an X and a Y (3)

5 'People pass _____ their characteristics to their children with only minor changes.' (2)

6 Opposite of recessive, gene-wise (8)

7 This delivers the DNA message (1,1,1)

8 Only males have this (1,10)

9 See 17 down

10 Daughter cells are produced by cell _____ (8)

12 If a gene or a complete organism is copied, it is _____ (6)

13 The science of heredity (8)

17 and 9 Find the complete genetic make-up of an organism: map _____ _____ (3,6)

Physics and physicists

physics
physicist

force
matter

Physics is the study of **matter**: the substances out of which the universe is made, and **forces**: the interactions between them.

universe *153* ⇓

People working in physics are **physicists**.

He does not mention the simplest world, which would consist of nothing whatsoever. There would be no space, no time, no laws of physics, and perhaps no mathematics and logic. To put it another way, there would be no universe.

space *153* ⇓

More than three centuries after Isaac Newton proposed his theory of gravity, physicists are still not sure how strong the force is.

Physicists confront the interesting idea that God, in the beginning, created matter and a few laws of physics, and then pushed it all off into space, saying, 'Goodbye and good luck'.

"WHAT AN EGO! ONE DAY IT'S NEWTON'S LAWS OF DYNAMICS, THEN IT'S NEWTON'S THEORY OF GRAVITATION, AND NEWTON'S LAW OF HYDRONAMIC RESISTANCE, AND NEWTON'S THIS AND NEWTON'S THAT."

1 Physics types. The words in the box often come in front of 'physics'.
Find combinations that refer to the study of:

1 the basic components of matter (2 expressions)   4 the physics of the atom nucleus
2 physics as a science based on calculation   5 physics for the 300 years before Einstein
3 physics as a science based on observation   6 solid matter

experimental

theoretical   quantum

physics

solid-state   Newtonian

particle   nuclear

Now match the two parts of these extracts.

a Paul Dirac was one of the founders of quantum physics, which was to alter people's
perception of the world, throwing up predictions that defied common sense.

b ...W and Z bosons. These two fundamental particles are crucial to the standard
model of particle physics,   model *21* ⇑

c Superconductivity – the disappearance of electrical resistance at extremely low
temperatures –

d Einstein's theory of relativity rules out such behaviour, because the velocity of the
particle must become greater than that of light.

e Within hours of the test Paul Vericel, director of the Centre d'Expérimentation du
Pacifique, said, 'We are not testing bombs.

f What about the Cambridge physicist who, earlier this century, was approached by a
young man who wanted to go into theoretical physics.

g This century has seen more of a separation between theoretical

i 'No future in it,' said our chap. 'It's all been sorted out. We now understand the
universe pretty well.'

ii and experimental physics, with the theoreticians winning most of the prizes.

iii Newtonian physics provides no such limit on the maximum speed of a particle.

iv is the single most tantalising item of ignorance in solid-state physics.

v the underlying theory of forces and matter that physicists now generally accept.

vi This physics, describing the very small, initially stole the limelight from Einstein's
relativity, the physics of the very big.

130   vii We are testing nuclear physics.'

Matter

element
compound

atom
atomic
  atomic structure

periodic table

molecule
molecular
  molecular structure

The basic types of substances into which matter can be broken down are the **elements**. Chemical combinations of elements are **compounds**.

Elements are characterized by the structure of their **atoms**. The related adjective is **atomic**. The nature of an element is determined by its **atomic structure**; elements are listed in the **periodic table** according to their atomic structure.

Atoms combine to form **molecules**. The related adjective is **molecular**. The nature of a combination of atoms is determined by its **molecular structure**.

Mendeleyev left gaps in the periodic table for the elements he expected to be discovered.

Each chemical element had its number and fixed position in the table, and from this it became possible to predict its behaviour: how it would react with other elements, what kind of compounds it would form, and what sort of physical properties it would have.

These special properties arise from the material's unique atomic structure. Diamond is a pure form of the element carbon. Its atoms are packed tightly together in a regular arrangement in which each one is surrounded by four others.

There are various ways to make atoms tangible. For chemists, the easiest thing is to tell a computer the positions of all the atoms that make up a molecule. The computer can then generate a three-dimensional likeness of the molecule.

Physicists and chemists still do not completely understand how molecules in these materials behave, but finding out would be a big step towards understanding the relation between their structure and dynamics. To explore solids and liquids at the atomic and molecular level, we need to look inside them.

…Kekule's sudden revelation of the molecular structure of benzene. What came to him as he sat dozing beside the fire, was the image of a snake biting its own tail, which gave him the idea that the structure could be ring-like instead of string-like.

2 **Atomic logic.** One key word from this section is missing from all these extracts. Which is it and what is its grammatical form?

The hard stuff. Visible light can cause	to react with each other. Shorter wavelengths
reason oil and water will not normally mix is that oil	(and things which dissolve in oil) are more attractive
however. Other scientists have been trying to join the	together. A strong, light material made from fused
you sniff a glass of wine, about 10m trillion odorous	get up your nose. Your brain senses a smooth,
region of India. Chemists know the structure of these	and understand fairly well how they affect quality.
Ozone is an unstable form of oxygen gas with	made up of three oxygen atoms rather than the usual
problem in astronomy. Kroto believed that these	must be formed in the atmospheres of giant carbon

States and properties

gas
liquid
solid

state

vacuum

property

Matter exists as **solids**, **liquids**, and **gases**. These are its basic possible **states**. There are others, as the first example indicates.

A space where there is no matter in any state is a **vacuum**.

The ways in which a substance behaves in different circumstances are its **properties**.

A new state of matter called a Luttinger liquid has been found by three teams of physicists in the US. In this state, electrons become linked, moving together like carriages in a train, rather than independently as they normally do.

To most people a material is a mixture of properties and substance; glass is transparent and made of sand. To scientists, materials are characterised by their microscopic structure; glasses are solids with no internal structure to the arrangement of their atoms. In this they are more like liquids than other solids.

The xenon atom is held onto the surface only by very weak chemical bonds. This means that the whole process has to take place at very low temperatures so that thermal vibrations do not bounce the xenon around, and in a vacuum so that gas molecules do not disturb it.

3 Property quiz. Choose the correct alternative to complete these statements. (In one case, two of the alternatives are correct. In all the others, only one is correct.)

1 If you can see very clearly through a material, the material is
   a translucent   b translucid   c transparent

2 If you cannot see through a material, it is
   a opal   b opalescent   c opaque

3 A substance that dissolves in liquid is
   a dissolute   b dissolvable   c soluble

4 A liquid that dissolves substances is a
   a solvent   b soluent   c solutent

5 A material that is hard but breaks easily is
   a battle   b brittle   c bristle

6 If a material bends easily, it is
   a bendible   b flexible   c flectable

7 A material that does not bend easily is
   a rancid   b rigorous   c rigid

8 A metal that can easily be beaten into new shapes is
   a beatable   b malleable   c mullible

9 A material that conducts electricity is
   a conducive   b conductive   c conductor

10 A material that catches fire easily is
   a flameable   b flammable   c inflammable

Changing states

celsius
centigrade
degrees C
degrees celsius
degrees centigrade

degrees K
degrees Kelvin
K

absolute zero

Temperatures are usually expressed in **degrees celsius** or **degrees centigrade**, abbreviated as **degrees C**.

Temperatures, especially extremely low ones, may be expressed in **degrees Kelvin**, abbreviated to **degrees K** or **K**, a scale which takes its starting point as **absolute zero**, the lowest temperature theoretically obtainable.

◆ **LANGUAGE NOTE**
Alternative spellings for **celsius** and **centigrade** are **Celsius** and
Centigrade.
Kelvin is also spelled **kelvin** in this context.
The word 'degrees' may be omitted whichever temperature scale is being
used.

This radiation heats the two inner planets to a temperature of many hundreds of
degrees celsius.

inner planets *167* ⇓

The deep sea is a highly preserving environment where the water temperature is just a few
degrees centigrade and little light can penetrate.

environment *31* ⇑

Driving much of the research is the need to find materials which can be used at temperatures higher
than 1400 degrees C.

The Russian reactor has already heated hydrogen gas to 3000 kelvin in tests.

In the past month, the National Institute of Standards and Technology has twice broken the record for
the coldest temperature reached in the laboratory. Late last month, one team reported cooling caesium
atoms to 700 nanokelvin, or 0.7 millionths of a degree above absolute zero.

4 Changes and temperatures. Read the examples and complete the
commentary using the key words.

Each silicon atom is attached to four oxygen atoms in a tetrahedron. This produces a molecular structure
which is not only remarkably stable under chemical attack but is also mechanically strong and has a
high melting point. These properties are all displayed by silicon dioxide (SiO2), variously known as
silica, sand or quartz.

If the pressure of air above the water is reduced, its boiling point also decreases. If it is put in a vacuum,
its boiling point is reduced to near zero degrees C.·

At room temperature and pressure, hydrogen is a gas with two atoms bound together to form a
molecule: H2. But squeezing it and then cooling it changes things. Like most gases, hydrogen first
liquefies and then solidifies.

In 1984, Canon started using amorphous silicon as a coating on the photosensitive drums of its
copying machines. To lay down the coating, it allows silicon vapour to condense on the metal.

Water must have circulated around the planet, evaporating from the oceans and falling as snow in the
polar regions.

Within hours of its entry, the probe melted down and finally vaporised in the intense heat of
Jupiter's lower atmosphere.

probe *165* ⇓

boiling point melting point	The temperature at which a solid becomes a liquid is its _ _ _ _ _ _ _ _ _ _ _ _ and the point at which a liquid becomes a gas is its _ _ _ _ _ _ _ _ _ _ _ _ .
condense evaporate liquefy solidify vapour vaporize	When a gas or liquid becomes a solid, it _ _ _ _ _ _ _ _ _ _ . When a gas or a solid becomes a liquid, it _ _ _ _ _ _ _ _ _ _ . When a substance becomes a gas or _ _ _ _ _ _ , it _ _ _ _ _ _ _ _ _ _ or _ _ _ _ _ _ _ _ ; if it returns to its previous state, it _ _ _ _ _ _ _ _ _ .

◆ **LANGUAGE NOTE**
Vapour is spelled **vapor** in American English.
Vaporize is also spelled **vaporise** in British English.

Solid-state physics

solid-state physics	The study of the properties of solids is **solid-state physics**.
alloy	Solids studied include **crystals**, solids whose molecules are in regular geometrical shapes, and **alloys**, combinations of different **metals**, such as copper and tin in bronze.
crystal crystalline metal metallic	The adjective relating to crystal is **crystalline** and the adjective relating to metal is **metallic**.
conductor insulator	A substance that conducts electricity is a **conductor**. One that does not is an **insulator**. (Substances can also be conductors and insulators in relation to heat.)
superconductivity superconductor	One that conducts electricity without resistance is a **superconductor**, possessing the property of **superconductivity**.

◆ **LANGUAGE NOTE**
Solid-state is also spelled without a hyphen.

The effect of increasing funding for particle physics is to starve other, perhaps more immediately useful areas of physics. Solid-state physics has paid dearly for this.

If a molten metal alloy can be cooled quickly enough, it can freeze into a solid before it has a chance to crystallise properly. Unlike normal metals or alloys, the resulting amorphous alloys have no crystalline structure on a scale of more than a few hundred atoms. They thus can have unique electronic and magnetic properties, but are hard to make because cooling has to be very rapid.

Pauling developed a method for predicting the way in which atoms might arrange themselves to give a crystal structure.

Helium is a non-metal, although the ending '-ium' is usually reserved for metallic elements.

In an ordinary conductor such as metal, vibrations of the atoms impede the flow of electrons that forms an electric current.

Diamond conducts heat nearly four times better than copper, yet it is a good electrical insulator.

A superconductor is a material that has no electrical or thermal resistance. Useful stuff.

French researchers claim to have achieved superconductivity at the relatively high temperature of 250K, or about the temperature of a cold night in Siberia.

5 **Some like it cold.** Put the sections of this article from the *New Scientist* into the correct order. (The first section is a and the last g.)

Wonderful properties

a ...Superconducting materials change from a normal electrical conductor to a superconductor at some critical 'transition temperature', which is usually well below ordinary temperatures.

b The situation changed dramatically in 1986 with the discovery by Bednorz and Müller of superconductivity near the relatively high temperature of 30K in a metal oxide, lanthanum barium copper oxide.

c No one understood why superconductivity should happen at all until 1957, when John Bardeen, Leon Cooper and Robert Schrieffer at the University of Illinois showed how it could happen. They envisaged a state in which the phonons – the vibrations of atoms in the solid – behaved in a curious way.

d Instead of scattering the conduction electrons, at a particular temperature – and hence energy – the phonons would cooperate by allowing electrons to form special 'Cooper' pairs that could transport electrical charge without resistance.

e But until 1986, the highest transition temperature was about 23K, for the niobium–germanium alloy Nb_3Ge, which is well below the boiling point of liquid nitrogen (77K), the lowest temperature for most practical applications.

f A Dutch physicist, Heike Kamerlingh Onnes, discovered superconductivity in 1911 in frozen mercury at a transition temperature of 4.15K and since then dozens of metals and alloys have been found to be superconducting.

g This was followed by the discovery of copper oxide ceramic materials with an even higher transition temperature of 125K. Apart from their relatively high transition temperatures, these materials are remarkable because ceramics are usually excellent insulators. ...

Mass

mass

inertia

velocity

momentum

accelerate
acceleration

The **mass** of a given amount of matter is perceived as its weight, or in terms of its **inertia**, its reluctance to move if stationary, or to change its motion if moving.

The speed of an object is its **velocity**. The **momentum** of an object is its velocity multiplied by its mass.

The **acceleration** of an object is the rate of increase in its speed when it **accelerates**.

What is mass? On an everyday scale, it seems easy enough to understand. The more matter there is in something, the heavier it is. But at smaller scales mass is not really understood at all.

The most intriguing problem centres on inertia - the property of matter that makes heavy things hard to get moving, but once moving, hard to stop.

The rotation of any object is measured in terms of angular momentum, which depends on the linear momentum (the object's mass multiplied by its velocity) and the distance of the object from the centre of rotation.

The resistance to motion, or inertia, we feel when we try to push an object is a result of trying to make it accelerate relative to the average distribution of all the matter in the Universe.

universe **153** ⇓

People are notoriously poor at estimating an object's acceleration.

mechanics
  Newtonian mechanics
  quantum mechanics

quantum theory

The study of the motion of objects is **mechanics**.

Newtonian mechanics relates to ordinary objects travelling relatively slowly, at much less than the speed of light.

Quantum mechanics or **quantum theory** relates to the behaviour of objects the size of atoms or less.

As Werner Heisenberg showed almost 70 years ago, the mechanics of the subatomic world meant that an uncertainty is attached to any measurement of physical properties such as energy.

In classical physics, using the laws of Newtonian mechanics, we can calculate the exact path taken by the ball in going from A to B. We can even calculate the position and speed of the ball at any instant while it was in flight.

law **24** ⇑

Quantum mechanics rules in single atoms, whereas notions like electricity conduction work in groups of millions of atoms.

Quantum theory proves, or allows for the probability, that time travel is possible even if we will not have the technology for some time.

6 **Logic of mechanics.** Complete this article from the *New Scientist* with the words listed. (a and c occur twice each, and b four times.)

a accelerate   b inertia   c velocity

The Trouble with Inertia

...Inertia is so familiar that its attributes seem beyond question, but they have perplexed scientists of the calibre of Einstein and Richard Feynman.

If an object is at rest, or moving at constant _____ (1), its _____ (2) remains hidden. But try to _____ (3) it and _____ (4) suddenly rears its head, fighting against the change in _____ (5). This is summed up in Newton's second law of motion: F = Ma, force equals _____ (6) times acceleration.

But where does the _____ (7) come from? Einstein believed that it was somehow induced in objects whenever they _____ (8) relative to the rest of the universe, though quite how this interaction worked he never made clear. ...

Energy

energy
kinetic energy
thermal energy
emit
radiation

Energy is the power that enables a system or machine to work.

Energy shows itself in different ways: for example, in **kinetic energy**, the energy of moving objects; and in **thermal energy**, in the heat produced by burning fuels such as coal or gas.

When energy is lost or **emitted** from a source, there is **radiation**.

radiation **40** ⇑

As Einstein realised early this century, mass is a form of energy: the two are interchangeable. So the masses of atoms and nuclei depend not only on the total mass of their constituents, but also on the energy that binds them together.

Gas is more efficient: 55% of its thermal energy can be converted into electricity. With coal, the ratio is one-third in older stations, 50% in ultra-modern ones.

The kinetic energy of a mountain-sized object travelling at 25 kilometres per second is enormous.

Electrons lose energy in the form of electromagnetic radiation as they travel on curved paths. The higher the energy of the electrons, or the tighter the curve, the more radiation they emit.

7 **A celebrated equation.** The word 'energy' has been omitted five times from this *Independent* article. Where does it go?

Mass is Energy

...A fast particle or spaceship will appear to get distorted in shape as an outside observer watches it speeding along. Under normal conditions, a spaceship just needs to apply more thrust to go faster. But if it is already at very high speeds, a curious effect takes over: the velocity can't go much higher than it is already, yet the being poured in can't just go away. What happens? The poured in ends up augmenting the solid mass of the spaceship itself.

This should sound suspiciously familiar. The mass growth is pretty small at first, just a tiny fraction of the poured in - what you get by dividing by c^2, where c^2 is the square of the speed of light. Turn that equation around and you get the more familiar form, that equals mass times c^2, or $e=mc^2$. ...

Particles 1

particle

nucleus

neutron
proton

atomic number
atomic weight
isotope

electron

ion
ionize

charge
charged

Atoms are made up of **particles** with different characteristics.

At the centre of an atom is its **nucleus**, made up of   nucleus 112 ⇑
particles called **protons** and **neutrons**.

The **atomic number** of an element is the number of protons
in each atom nucleus. Its **atomic weight** is a measure of the
atom's mass.

Different **isotopes** of an element are atoms of that element
with the same number of protons in their nuclei but different
numbers of neutrons.

Surrounding the nucleus are particles called **electrons**. Atoms
that have gained or lost electrons have been **ionized** and are
ions.

Interactions between particles depends on their electric
charge: the way they are **charged**, positively or negatively.

◆ **LANGUAGE NOTE**
The plural form of **nucleus** is **nuclei**.
Ionize is also spelled **ionise** in British English.

*Nature provides 92 elements, ranging from hydrogen with
one positively charged <u>proton</u> in its <u>nucleus</u>, to uranium,
with 92 protons and 146 <u>neutrons</u>, <u>particles</u> with more or
less the same mass as a proton, but no electric <u>charge</u>.*

*Atoms can be thought of as miniature
solar systems, with a nucleus at the centre and*   solar system 167 ⇓
electrons orbiting at specific distances from it.   orbit 157 ⇓
*Electrons, being negatively <u>charged</u>, usually orbit as
close as possible to the positively charged nucleus.*

*If you make atoms hot enough, they shed their electrons
and become <u>ions</u>; the ions and electrons produce a plasma,
the sort of fire that is seen in the sun.*

*The temperature at the centre rose above 2000 degrees C,
breaking up the molecules of hydrogen and then <u>ionising</u>
both the hydrogen and helium atoms.*

Tin has been found floating in the space between the stars. The element, which has <u>atomic number</u>   star 175 ⇓
50, is by far the heaviest ever found in the interstellar medium.   interstellar 175 ⇓

*Because these particles are of low <u>atomic weight</u>, X-rays pass straight through them. Uranium atoms
come in two types; there is a heavy <u>isotope</u>, uranium-238, and a light isotope, uranium-235.*

8 Top table. Read this article from the *New Scientist* and answer the questions.

Elementary, my dear Mendeleyev

Chemistry without the periodic table is as hard to imagine as sailing without a compass.

...As news of his remarkable accomplishment spread, Mendeleyev became something of a hero, and interest in the periodic table soared. In all, Mendeleyev predicted 10 new elements, of which all but two turned out to exist. He later proposed that the positions of some pairs of adjacent elements be reversed to make their properties fit into the periodic pattern.

He suggested swapping cobalt with nickel and argon with potassium, which he believed had been wrongly placed because their atomic weights were different from the values chemists had determined.

It took until 1913, some six years after Mendeleyev had died to clear up this ambiguity. By then chemists had gained a much better understanding of the atom, and in that year, Henry Moseley showed that the position of an element in the table is governed not by its atomic weight but by its atomic number.

The atomic number of an element defines the number of protons in its atomic nucleus, which in a neutral atom is equal to the number of electrons surrounding it. Moseley proved that the characteristic frequency of the X-rays generated by a particular element is directly related to its atomic number.

One source of confusion for Mendeleyev was that the atomic weight that chemists measure is an average of the slightly different weights of all the different isotopes of an element.

Mendeleyev's intuition had been right, however, and atomic number was used successfully to assign a place in an expanded table for the noble gases - helium, neon, argon, krypton, radon and xenon - which had been discovered in the 1890s. ...

1 How many of the new elements predicted by Mendeleyev are now known to exist?

2 Mendeleyev suggested that cobalt and nickel should change p _ _ _ _ _ s in the table.

3 If X is governed by Y, is it dictated by Y?

4 If X is characteristic of Y, is it typical of Y?

5 These gases are called 'noble' because they were a) discovered by aristocrats, or b) originally thought not to form parts of compounds and are thus 'superior' to other gases.

Particles 2

particle
elementary particle
fundamental particle
sub-atomic particle
wave

The particles making up atoms are often referred to as **elementary particles**, **fundamental particles**, or **sub-atomic particles**.

Sub-atomic theory is concerned with particles and **waves**. A wave is a disturbance that travels from one place to another through matter or space.

The neutron was first identified by James Chadwick at the Cavendish Laboratory, Cambridge, in 1932. It was the first electrically neutral <u>elementary particle</u> to be identified; previously, only the positively charged proton and negatively charged electron were known.

Physicists are homing in on yet another of the <u>fundamental particles</u> of matter. In what may be the largest single calculation ever performed by a computer, they have worked out the properties to be expected of objects known as 'glueballs'. As their name implies, glueballs are the things that stick other particles together.

There are various pairs of properties which quantum mechanics says cannot both be subjected to precise measurement at the same time. One such pair is the position and velocity of a <u>sub-atomic particle</u>. If, for example, you have a good fix on its velocity, then you cannot know where it is, not because you are not clever enough, but because its position is indeterminate.

Quantum theory says that light is simultaneously a <u>wave</u> and a stream of particles called photons.

atom smasher
particle accelerator
antiatom
antimatter
antiparticle

Quantum research depends greatly on **particle accelerators**, machines that accelerate particles to very high velocities so that their properties can be analysed. Particle accelerators are also referred to by journalists as **atom smashers**.

Particle accelerators are used to study not only matter, but also the **antiparticles** that make up **antiatoms**, the basis of **antimatter**, as the example explains.

◆ LANGUAGE NOTE

Antiatom, **antimatter**, and **antiparticle** are also spelled with hyphens.

<u>Atom smashers</u> of ever-greater power have produced a theory, the Standard Model, which works well in explaining the nature of matter and the forces that hold it together.   **model 21** ⇑

The LEP is one of the most powerful <u>particle accelerators</u> in the world. Housed in a gigantic circular tunnel, it spans the border between Switzerland and France. Its powerful magnets keep high-energy beams of electrons and positrons flying around the ring before smashing them into one another. Physicists then pore over the debris of these collisions in search of the fundamental building blocks of the Universe.

universe 153 ⇓

The time has come for physicists to take a step up from <u>antiparticles</u> to <u>antiatoms</u>. They are looking at ways of bringing the <u>antimatter</u> counterpart of electrons, called positrons, and antiprotons close enough for long enough to form stable antihydrogen atoms.

9 Fleeting creations. Read the article from *The Times* below and in it find equivalent expressions to the numbered expressions listed. (The words occur in the same order as the questions. The number of letters for each word is given in brackets, along with the paragraph it occurs in.)

1 things that look exactly like other things (13; paragraph 1)
2 matter or material (5; paragraph 1)
3 describing something that looks exactly the same as something else, but with reversed symmetry (6–5; paragraph 2)
4 common (11; paragraph 3)
5 features (15; paragraph 3)
6 identical to (17, 4; paragraph 4)
7 destroyed (11; paragraph 5)

Shadowy Doppelgangers

...Physicists at the European Particle Physics laboratory in Geneva have created anti-atoms, shadowy doppelgangers of hydrogen, the stuff of which the universe is mostly made. These fugitive anti-atoms lasted the barest millionths of a second, and could only be detected by the process of smashing them to pieces once more and observing the wreckage.

The first suggestion that matter might exist in a kind of mirror-image form came from the physicist Paul Dirac more than 60 years ago. He predicted the existence of the positron, a particle identical with the electron - but with a positive rather than a negative charge.

It turned out that positrons were really quite commonplace, being formed by the decay of some radioactive isotopes and by the impact of cosmic rays on the atmosphere. Physicists found they could be made by bombarding materials with electrons, and a family of anti-particles followed - anti-protons, anti-neutrinos and others. They have the same mass as their opposite numbers but the electrical charges and other characteristics are reversed. ...

cosmic *179* ⇓

The one particle which is indistinguishable from its anti-matter particle is the photon, the particle of light. This means that a world made of anti-matter would appear no different to us from the one made of real matter.

It is possible, if unlikely, that there are objects in space - whole galaxies even - that appear outwardly normal but are not made of matter but anti-matter. A spaceman visiting such an anti-world would be instantly annihilated, as his matter met an equal mass of anti-matter.

space *153* ⇓
galaxy *177* ⇓

All that would be left would be a burst of gamma-rays, because matter and anti-matter cancel each other out, their mass converted to energy according to Einstein's famous equation, $e=mc^2$. ...

Nuclear fission

nuclear
nuclear fission
chain reaction
split the atom
critical mass

Things relating to the nucleus of the atom are **nuclear**.

Nuclear fission releases energy by breaking down the nucleus of uranium or plutonium atoms in a **chain reaction**. This is sometimes referred to, especially by journalists, as **splitting the atom**.

The minimum amount of uranium or plutonium required for such a reaction is the **critical mass**.

In the space of a few months, the number of known fundamental particles doubled from two to four; the atoms of the lighter elements, far from being indivisible, were broken open at will; and powerful new machinery for both producing and detecting the particles came into use. These discoveries gave <u>nuclear</u> physics a new impulse.

Scientific knowledge is value-free. Which means that just because you know how to <u>split the atom</u>, it doesn't necessarily follow that you must kill people with an atom bomb.

Splitting the atoms all at once might not be so hard. The neutrons given off when the atoms came apart - a process called <u>fission</u> - could split more atoms in turn. In a lump the right size and shape - a <u>critical mass</u> - every neutron produced would stand a good chance of hitting and splitting another nucleus. The chain reaction would lead, in the right circumstances, to a vast explosion.

If we could find an element which is split by neutrons and which would emit two neutrons when it absorbed one neutron, such an element, if assembled in a sufficiently large mass, could sustain a nuclear <u>chain reaction</u>. The chain reaction would give rise to a potentially huge amount of energy.

nuclear energy
nuclear power
nuclear weapons

Fission is the source of energy used to generate electricity: **nuclear energy** or **nuclear power**; and of bombs and other arms: **nuclear weapons**.

nuclear energy *40* ⇑
nuclear power *40* ⇑

France now relies on <u>nuclear energy</u> for 75% of its electricity, compared with 19% in America, 28% in Japan and 33% in Europe as a whole.

It is hard not to believe that if the cash thrown at <u>nuclear power</u> had been put into almost any other technology, it would have eventually produced something commercially viable.

After the blast at Hiroshima, Rotblat and a group of nuclear physicists began to advocate control of <u>nuclear weapons</u>.

radioactive
radioactivity

decay

half-life

fallout

Radioactivity is the emission by **radioactive** substances of energy in the form of harmful rays.

radioactive *40* ⇑
radioactivity *40* ⇑

The atoms of radioactive elements **decay** to produce other elements. The time it takes for half of a particular quantity of a radioactive material to decay in this way is its **half-life**. Half of the remaining quantity will decay in the following period of the same duration, and so on.

Radioactivity spreading after the explosion of a nuclear weapon is **fallout**.

◆ **LANGUAGE NOTE**
Decay is both a noun and a verb.
Fallout is also spelled with a hyphen.

The Nirex repository will hold plutonium whose <u>radioactivity</u> will scarcely diminish over 10,000 years.

Acord learnt that he could capture fast neutrons and use them to transmute the nuclear waste product technetium-99, a highly <u>radioactive</u> gamma emitter that has a <u>half-life</u> of 212,000 years, into ruthenium-100, which is stable.

waste *34* ⇑

Radiocarbon dating estimates the age of a sample of organic material from the amount of radioactive carbon-14 it contains. The older a sample, the more time its carbon-14 has had to <u>decay</u> (half the carbon is lost every 5,730 years) and the smaller the proportion of this isotope compared with the two stable isotopes, carbon-12 and carbon-13.

Americium is highly radioactive, emitting alpha particles and gamma rays as it transmutes to neptunium. It has a half-life of 430 years; in other words, half of the sample will undergo radioactive <u>decay</u> during this time.

The plutonium fission bomb has left few traces. A 1,200-foot crater has long since been filled in and radioactive <u>fallout</u> removed by the Atomic Energy Commission.

10 **Nuclear combinations.** The words in the box often come after 'nuclear'. Divide them into two groups of six expressions each, those that relate to:

1 nuclear energy
2 nuclear weapons

stations

plant   test

disarmament   industry

proliferation   **nuclear**   fuel

waste   reactor

warhead   arsenal

explosion

Nuclear fusion

nuclear fusion

cold fusion

Nuclear fusion is the combining of two lightweight atomic nuclei at very high temperatures to produce energy.

Some physicists say that this can be done at low temperatures in a process of **cold fusion**.

"NO, THIS ISN'T LOW TEMPERATURE PHYSICS. HE'S JUST TOO CHEAP TO TURN ON THE HEAT."

Cold fusion, said Fleischmann, could lead to a cheap and potentially limitless supply of energy. The claim was widely denounced as being fanciful, unrepeatable and unscientific, mainly by physicists convinced that <u>nuclear fusion</u> could only be achieved in huge reactors containing gases heated to temperatures approaching those of the Sun.

sun *167* ⇓

11 **The promise of clean energy.** Read this article from *The Economist* and complete each space in the table with 'yes', 'no', or 'not mentioned'. (The first line has been completed for you.)

At the Going Down of the Nuclear Sun

Nuclear fusion promises to be an exciting and elegant way to generate power, but it is no more of a panacea than nuclear fission has been.

...Although both are nuclear reactions, fusion and fission are very different beasts. Small atomic nuclei will give up energy if clumped together. That is fusion. Large nuclei will give up energy if broken apart. That is fission. All elements except iron, which is perfectly happy to stay as it is, can in principle be made to release energy in one or other of these ways. In practice, fusion works best with very light nuclei, fission with very heavy ones.

Some heavy nuclei are unstable. If you hit one with a neutron, it will break up into smaller nuclei and more neutrons. These neutrons can go on to hit other nuclei in turn. Get enough such nuclei close together and the knock-ons will produce a chain reaction. Unfortunately, the heavy elements required, uranium and plutonium, normally are expensive and rare, and the new nuclei produced are radioactive and dangerous. Worst of all the chain reaction can spin out of control, leading to a meltdown.

Fission is reasonably simple to start. The first fission reactor, built on a squash court in Chicago under the guidance of Enrico Fermi, worked first time. But - witness Chernobyl - it can be hard to stop. Fusion, on the other hand, is hard to get started. While fissile nuclei are eager to fall apart, those which might fuse are loath to get close enough together to do so.

To bring two light nuclei close enough to fuse means overcoming their natural repulsion. They have to be moving fast, which means they have to be hot - hence the term thermonuclear to describe fusion reactors and their untamed relations - hydrogen bombs. Getting things hot enough while keeping them under control is hard. But if you can arrange it, the result will be more attractive than a fission reactor in a number of ways.

The first has to do with the fuel. First-generation fusion reactors will use a mixture of deuterium and tritium, heavy forms of hydrogen that contain extra neutrons. Deuterium is plentiful in the oceans. Tritium can be manufactured by splitting lithium nuclei in half with neutrons, which is easily done in most sorts of nuclear reactor, and could be done in a fusion reactor. So fuel is not much of a problem.

Nor is the exhaust. The end product of a fusion reaction is not a pile of radioactive muck. It is helium, a harmless gas. ...

	Fission	Fusion
Works well with light elements	no	yes
Works well with heavy elements		
Nuclei produced in reaction are dangerous		
Reaction is easy to start		
Reaction is easy to stop		
Fuel is easily obtainable		
Produces radioactive waste		

Forces

force

electromagnetism
gravitation
gravity
strong interaction
strong nuclear force
weak interaction
weak nuclear force

grand unified theory
GUT

A **force** is an effect of attraction or repulsion between two bodies or particles.

The four forces are:

gravity or **gravitation**, the attraction of objects towards each other because of their mass.

electromagnetism, electrical effects binding matter or pushing it apart.

the **strong interaction** or **strong nuclear force**.

the **weak interaction** or **weak nuclear force**.

These last two, sub-atomic, forces are explained in the examples.

Physicists are attempting to explain the latter three of these forces in **grand unified theories**, or **GUTs**.

The less dense the universe, the less the force of gravity will tend to slow its expansion as time goes by. **universe 153** ⇓

A falling apple is one thing, the gracious progress of a distant planet quite another. That, at least was the situation before Newton came along with universal gravitation. The glory of his idea was that it explained these two phenomena in terms of one theory. **planet 167** ⇓ **phenomenon 17** ⇑ **theory 21** ⇑

At the US Open tennis tournament this week, a system that may finally end disputes over line calls will be put to the test. Unlike existing line sensors, which rely on a ball breaking a laser beam, the new system is based on electromagnetism. Tennis balls impregnated with 5 grams of iron powder are detected by electrodes buried beneath the lines of the court.

Before 1932, physicists knew of only two forces of nature, gravity and electromagnetism. Protons and neutrons in nuclei are now understood to be held together by another force, the strong interaction.

Gauge theories describe forces in terms of 'gauge bosons', particles which transmit forces between other particles. In the 1960s, gauge theorists began to have some success in their understanding of the weak interaction, the force which occasionally turns a neutron into a proton, an electron and a neutrino. **theorist 21** ⇑

The search for proton decay was sparked off in the 1970s by the grand unified theories which attempt to explain at a single stroke the common origins of the strong and weak nuclear forces and electromagnetism. According to these theories, the proton, and consequently all matter, cannot be immortal.

12 **Theories of everything.** Read this article from *The Economist* and complete it using the words listed. (a occurs four times, c three times, b and d twice each.)

a force   b forces   c particle   d particles

The **Big** Picture

...Within a second of creation, the universe reached a state about which there is plenty of agreement. It was small, immensely hot and filled with a dense soup of the fundamental _____ (1): quarks (which are heavy) and leptons (which are light). It is this state that fascinates _____ (2) physicists. Their passion is the unification of _____ (3).

Today's universe contains four observable _____ (4): the electromagnetic and gravitational ones, which work over long ranges, and the weak and strong nuclear ones, which work only locally.

Inside _____ (5) accelerators it is possible to show that the weak _____ (6) and electromagnetism are two parts of a single 'electro-weak' _____ (7). Above a certain energy, the difference between electromagnetism and the weak _____ (8) vanishes. The next aim for _____ (9) physics is to find a theory that unites the strong _____ (10) with the electro-weak interaction.

Such a grand unified theory (GUT) would describe phenomena that take place at energies unobtainable in any accelerator. It would also describe the behaviour of the quarks and other _____ (11) immediately after the big bang. So one way to sort out the various GUTs is to see which can be used to tell believable and, ideally, testable stories about the big bang. ...

big bang *179* ⇓

Space-time

space-time	**Space-time** encompasses the usual three dimensions and a fourth dimension, time.
relativity	Space-time is a fundamental concept in theories of **relativity**.

◆ **LANGUAGE NOTE**
 Space-time is also spelled as one word.

The cornerstone of the special theory of <u>relativity</u> is the notion that the speed of light in space is always the same wherever it is measured from, and however fast and in whatever direction the person measuring it is moving. This leads to the conclusion that energy and mass are interchangeable and that no object can travel faster than light.

Relativity combines space and time into <u>spacetime</u>, which can be distorted in various ways. These distortions explain, among other things, the force of gravity.

13 Distorted thinking. Read this article from the *New Scientist* and answer the questions.

Curved Space-Time

After Einstein had developed his special theory, his thoughts turned to describing how objects behave when accelerated and under the influence of gravity. The need for a description of curved space-time to explain gravity came to him with the realisation that a person falling from a roof does not feel the force of gravity. This led Einstein to think about how light might fall under the influence of gravity, which can be simply explained in terms of a 'thought experiment' involving a lift.

People in a falling lift will float, completely weightless, able to push themselves from wall to wall or floor to ceiling. Because the acceleration of the lift, plunging downwards at an ever increasing speed, can precisely cancel out the force of gravity, the force and the acceleration must be exactly equivalent to one another.

Imagine setting up an experiment in such a lift to measure the behaviour of a beam of light that crosses from one side of the lift to the other. In a lift moving at a constant velocity, far from any planet or star, the light will travel in a straight line across the lift.

But in the accelerated lift, the opposite wall has speeded up and moved forward (down) relative to the light beam in the time it takes the light to cross the lift. The only way in which it can look as if the light is following a straight line, from the point of view of the people in the lift, will be if the trajectory of the beam of light is bent by gravity.

Since light has no mass, how can it be affected by gravity? The answer is that what we think of as forces caused by the presence of lumps of matter, such as the Sun, are distortions in the fabric of space-time.

The Sun, for example, makes a dent in the geometry of space-time, and the orbit that the Earth makes around the Sun is a result of trying to follow the shortest path through space-time. ...

theory **21** ⇑

1 If your thoughts turn to something, do you start thinking about it?

2 Do thought experiments need to be done in laboratories?

thought experiment **13** ⇑

3 If X cancels out Y, is it equal to Y?

4 If you set up an experiment, you a) prepare it, b) prove it, or c) disprove it.

5 If something speeds up, it
a _ _ _ _ _ _ _ _ s .

6 The trajectory of something is its
r o _ _ e .

7 If something is distorted, is it regular?

sun **167** ⇓

orbit **157** ⇓

Crossword

Across

2 and 6 Smaller than atoms (3–6,9)

9 Space and _____ are relative (4)

10 9 across is part of this theory (10)

13 Nuclear fission is 'splitting _____ atom' (3)

14 Particles can be this, positively or negatively (7)

16 The G of GUT (5)

17 Colder than this you can't get (8,4)

18 This produces energy and makes weapons (7)

19 Radioactive decay is measured using half of this (4)

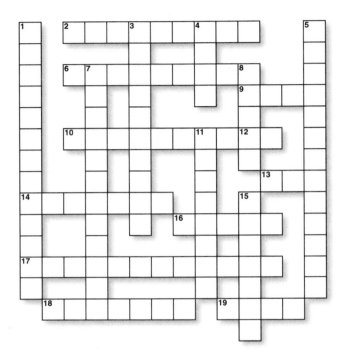

Down

1 One of four: the _____ _____ force (6,7)

3 When matter meets this, there is annihilation (10)

4 When a solid liquefies, it _____s (4)

5 The energy of motion (7,6)

7 Smashers (12)

8 Gas, for example, is a _____ (5)

11 When liquids boil, they do this (8)

15 Hard to get moving and hard to stop: phenomena of _____ (7)

7 Space

Space and the universe

space
  outer space

universe

astronomer
astronomical
astronomy

astrophysical
astrophysicist
astrophysics

Space or **outer space** is the area beyond the earth and its atmosphere, and the objects it contains.

The **universe** is space viewed as a whole, and the matter and energy in it.

matter *129* ⇑
energy *139* ⇑

The study of objects in space is **astronomy**; its specialists are **astronomers**. The related adjective is **astronomical**.

Astrophysics is the application of physical theories to explain the nature and behaviour of phenomena in space. People doing this are **astrophysicists**. The related adjective is **astrophysical**.

◆ **LANGUAGE NOTE**
An alternative spelling for **universe** is **Universe**.

Space is not all that far away - 300 kilometres above you.

Mankind is set to boldly step up the search for life in outer space with the launch of a new mission to identify Earth-like planets that may support forms of life.

There follows a brief account of astrophysical methods by which the age of the Universe has been estimated.

The comet, baptised McNaught-Russel, was recognised officially by the International Astronomical Union, which names such bodies.

…the central problem of modern astronomy: the fact that although astronomers see only those things that give off light or some other radiation, theory and circumstance tell them that this universe is dominated by matter which makes no such display.

Some might even go as far as to say that physics is now a subset of astrophysics.

Astrophysicists work in a laboratory the size of the whole universe, where matter can be studied under extreme conditions not available on earth.

1 Space combinations. The words in the box often come after 'space'.
Find combinations that refer to:

1 the present period of human activity in space

2 a government organization that deals with space

3 the activities in space of a particular country or organization

4 making journeys into space

5 going to new places in space and finding out about them

6 the rivalry that existed in space between the United States and the former Soviet Union

7 the remains of man-made objects in space

---

	race	
	agency	age
exploration	**space**	programme
	debris	travel

Now use these words to complete the extracts below.

a Yuri Gagarin's first orbit of the earth began the real space _____ .

b NASA (National Aeronautics and Space Administration) has finally acknowledged that
the space _____ is over. Last week the _____ announced plans to cut much
of its bureaucracy, shedding 30,000 jobs and trimming $5 billion from its budget by the
end of the decade. The cuts will leave NASA with a smaller workforce than at any time
since 1961.

c One piece of the Russian Salyut 7 space station was reported to have fallen into the back
garden of a house where an Argentine woman was doing her ironing. So far, however,
there are no known human victims of space _____ and the only confirmed
casualty was a cow in Cuba that was killed by a falling rocket motor in the 1960s.

d NASA scientists first used the term cyborg to describe the technological
enhancement of the human body for space _____ , proposing a combination
of drugs and surgery to enable humans to survive in the harsh environment of outer
space.

    drug *87* ⇑
    surgery *97* ⇑

e ...the President's declared intention that the US should return to the Moon and go on to
Mars: the Space _____ Initiative.

f A US ban on the sale of space technology to India will affect the Indian space
_____ only 'a little bit', according to U R Rao, head of the Indian Space Research
Organisation.

Launching spacecraft

launch
launch pad

launch vehicle
launcher

spaceport

rocket

blast off
blast-off
lift off
lift-off

craft
spacecraft

Objects are **launched** into space from **launch pads** using **launchers** or **launch vehicles**, usually **rockets**.

A launch pad and its facilities are sometimes referred to by journalists as a **spaceport**.

The moment during a launch when the launcher leaves the launch pad is **blast-off** or **lift-off**: the launcher **blasts off** or **lifts off**.

Rockets and other space vehicles are **craft** or **spacecraft**. Rockets and spacecraft often have names, such as Apollo and Energia.

◆ **LANGUAGE NOTE**
Launch is a noun and a verb.
Launch pad is also spelled with a hyphen.
As nouns, **blast-off** and **lift-off** are also spelled as one word.
Spaceport and **spacecraft** are also spelled with a hyphen and as two words.
Craft is both the singular and plural form, but the plural form **crafts** is sometimes used.

A private, unmanned <u>rocket</u> carrying scientific experiments into space destroyed itself moments after <u>lift-off</u> from a new NASA <u>launch</u> site on the coast of Virginia.

Reiter and his Russian colleagues are scheduled for <u>blast-off</u> at midday aboard a Soyuz TM-71 rocket from the <u>launch-pad</u> used by Yuri Gagarin in 1961.

It burns liquid hydrogen fuel, trickier to handle than the kerosene and nitrogen tetroxide all other liquid-fuelled <u>launchers</u> use in their first-stage engines.

Goldin doesn't believe in 'Big Space' projects. 'I don't want any more billion-dollar, multi-year programmes where you lose everything if you lose the <u>launch vehicle</u>,' he says.

The shuttle Atlantis <u>blasted off</u> from Florida yesterday, for a historic meeting with the Russian space station Mir.

CHINESE ROCKET EXPLODES MINUTES AFTER <u>LIFTING OFF</u>.

In November the first of its new Ariane 5s should be on its way into orbit from the <u>spaceport</u> in Kourou, French Guiana.

NASA estimates that to assemble Alpha, astronauts will have to stay outside their <u>crafts</u> for 400 hours.

Russia's rockets are the greatest achievement of the country's space industry. They have launched over 2,000 spacecraft; they are mass-produced and highly reliable.

thrust	A launcher's power or **thrust** is provided by its engines, which use fuel or **propellant**.
propellant	Launchers consist of several **stages**: when there is no more propellant in one stage, it falls away and thrust is provided by the next stage. One of these stages may be called a **booster**.
booster	
stage	

Launching the shuttle demands a thrust of around 30 million Newtons, or a force equivalent to a ground weight of 3000 tonnes.

force 129 ⇑

Ariane 5's first flight was pushed back six months after problems in solidifying the 237 tonnes of rubber-like propellant for the booster.

The four-stage, solid-fuelled Taurus rocket can be driven about on a trailer and set up for launch almost anywhere.

2 **Powerful propulsion.** Complete this article from the *New Scientist* with the words listed. (a occurs five times, b twice, and c and d once each.)

a rocket   b rockets   c propellant   d thrust

Pentagon Reveals Secret Nuclear-Powered Rocket

The Pentagon revealed last week that it is working on a _____ (1) powered by a nuclear reactor. ... The US air force's Phillips Laboratory, in Albuquerque, New Mexico, is in charge of the project, which is known officially as the Space Nuclear Thermal Propulsion programme. Roger Lenard, an air force officer who is managing the programme, says that a nuclear _____ (2) may be a cheaper way to lift heavy loads into orbit.

In a nuclear engine, liquid hydrogen is the _____ (3). It is pumped into the core of a reactor, where the heat turns it instantly into a gas, with explosive force. This drives the _____ .

_____ (4) forward, and the hot hydrogen gas escapes from the rear.

The lighter the atomic weight of the fuel used by a _____ (5) engine, the more efficiently it produces its _____ (6). In theory, a _____ (7) using only hydrogen would be more than twice as efficient as _____ (8) that rely on chemical combustion, which also require oxygen.

Lenard points out that nuclear _____ (9) could make an expedition to Mars more feasible. Some calculations show that nuclear propulsion could cut the time required for a return trip to Mars from 400 days to about 200. ...

nuclear 144 ⇑

liquid 132 ⇑

gas 132 ⇑

Putting payloads into orbit

payload

satellite

orbit
  geostationary orbit
  geosynchronous orbit

single stage to orbit
SSTO

reusable launch vehicle
RLV

The object that a launch vehicle puts into space is its **payload**.

One of the uses of launch vehicles is to put **satellites** into **orbit** round the earth. (Compare this with 'satellite' in the section on the sun and the planets below.)

If a satellite orbits the earth so that it appears to be fixed in one place above the earth, it is in **geostationary orbit** or **geosynchronous orbit**.

One-stage launch vehicles that in future may be able to put payloads into orbit are described as **single stage to orbit**, or **SSTO**. A launch vehicle able to take off and land repeatedly is a **reusable launch vehicle** or **RLV**.

The latest version of its three-stage launcher, called the M-3SII, can put a 770 kg payload into low orbit round the earth or 130 kg into orbit round the sun.

Brazil's first satellite was launched last week by a Pegasus rocket.

If a satellite orbits the earth at 37,000 km, it goes round once every 24 hours, and thus appears to hover in the sky. This 'geostationary' orbit holds almost all today's communications satellites, strung out round the equator like pearls.

Hipparcos was meant to sit in a geosynchronous orbit, following a fixed point above the equator. The booster failure left Hipparcos in a highly elliptical orbit, swooping to within 500 km of the earth, then soaring 36,000 km into space every 10 hours.

…the Single Stage to Orbit, a reusable rocket being developed by NASA. The SSTO is designed to provide a cheap way to launch satellites, but it would only be able to carry satellites into low orbits.

NASA has selected three teams of aerospace companies to develop competing concepts for the new spacecraft, or Reusable Launch Vehicle (RLV). Late next year, the agency will pick one or two of the teams to build small-scale versions of the designs to demonstrate their technologies.

3 Launch pad or launch rig? Read this article from the *New Scientist* and answer the questions.

Strange Allies Launch Floating Spaceport

...An unlikely alliance of aerospace companies from Russia, Ukraine and the US is hoping to break into the satellite launch market with a seagoing launch pad. The companies are negotiating to buy a second-hand oil drilling platform which they want to convert into a floating spaceport operating in the mid-Pacific. From there the group, called Sea Launch, would be able to launch satellites into a much wider range of orbits than their competitors.

The US aircraft manufacturer Boeing is coordinating the project. It says Sea Launch is planning its first blastoff early in 1998, although it has yet to sign up a single customer.

A launch from mid-ocean avoids the problem of spent rocket stages falling to Earth in populated areas. Cape Canaveral in Florida, for instance, cannot launch satellites into orbits that pass over the poles because debris would fall on Florida. Also, a floating launch pad can be operated from the equator, where launches are much more efficient. The extra speed from the Earth's rotation means that customers can launch more for their money.

The heart of the Sea Launch system is the Zenit rocket, manufactured by NPO Yuzhnoye of Ukraine, and originally built as an intercontinental nuclear missile. The Zenit has been used as a space launcher at the Baikonur Cosmodrome in Kazakhstan and was part of the Soviet Union's now defunct Energia heavy-lift rocket.

The Zenit will serve as the first and second stages of the Sea Launch rocket. The third stage, which will carry satellites to orbits high above the equator, is to be provided by the Russian company RSC Energia.

Sea Launch will be able to carry payloads of 16,000 kilograms into a low altitude orbit, or 5,900 kg into an orbit high above the equator. ...

1 Which expression is used later in the article to refer to a specific spaceport in the former Soviet Union?

2 Does the project have clients?

3 If a rocket stage is spent, is it still producing thrust?

4 What expression used earlier in the article does 'debris' replace?

5 If something is defunct, does it still exist?

6 Could the word 'altitude' be omitted here without any change in meaning?

Satellites

telecommunications satellite
satellite dish
satellite television
beam

Satellites are of different kinds. **Telecommunications satellites** amplify signals from earth and retransmit them to earth, for example to **satellite dishes**, to provide **satellite television** services.

Satellites like these **beam** TV programmes to a given area.

Other types of satellites are shown in the exercise.

Thomson thinks they are opting for a technique pioneered by the Soviet Union to give continuous telecommunications in the far north beyond the reach of conventional <u>telecommunications satellites</u> which orbit the equator. The technique requires a handful of satellites in highly elliptical orbits. **pioneer 28** ⇑

'France,' Mr Toubon said, 'refuses to consider the English language as an inevitability.' Technology, however, may give France no choice. <u>Satellite television</u> means that the English-language programmes of America's CNN and NBC Superchannel, as well as Britain's BSkyB and the BBC, are all available to any European prepared to make a modest investment in a receiving dish and decoder.

Danish engineers beam the code up in a narrow beam to the Intelsat satellite serving the North Atlantic Area, then it is <u>beamed</u> down again in a very wide beam which just reaches Greenland. The coded signal is received by the 11-metre <u>satellite dish</u> aerials installed at all the TV transmitters across Greenland and up to the Arctic Circle. Although the signal is very weak, it is still just distinguishable from background noise and thus can be decoded into a perfect TV picture.

4 Satellite types. The expressions in the box often come in front of 'satellite'. Match the two parts of each extract containing them.

> spy
>
> weather   reconnaissance
>
> communications   **satellite**   observation
>
> navigation   global positioning

1   The geostationary communications satellites used for telecommunications traffic today orbit the earth at an altitude of around 36,000 kilometres.

2   The spy satellites gave the West a vital view of events in the Soviet Union and China.

3   Each car is equipped with a receiver whose position is continuously pinpointed by satellites orbiting the earth.

4   The climate works according to the established rules of physics, chemistry and biology.

5   There are six optical-reconnaissance satellites in the Keyhole series currently thought to be in orbit.

6   The first satellite, which will be called Envisat-1,

7   America's navigation satellites send out messages

a   They produce images good enough to make out an object the size of a paperback book.

b   that allow anyone with a receiver to work out where he is to within 100 metres.

c   The collection includes a picture of the Kremlin in which the queue of people waiting to see Lenin's tomb is clearly visible.

d   The global positioning satellite receiver is linked to a unit with a digitalised map.

e   In contrast, a low Earth-orbit satellite (LEOS) flies just a few hundred kilometres up.

f   What is needed is the data to make clear what is going on where; satellites are uniquely suited to provide this information. Weather satellites have already greatly improved forecasting.

g   will follow on from the Earth observation satellites ERS-1 and ERS-2, studying the Earth's surface and the environment.

data 17 ⇑

Manned flight

space flight
space mission

manned flight
manned mission

astronaut
cosmonaut

Space flights are referred to as **missions**. The crews of **manned flights** or **manned missions** are **astronauts**.

Astronauts from the former Soviet Union are **cosmonauts**.

"I MUST SAY IT ISN'T EASY ADJUSTING TO A 24-SECOND DAY."

From Russia comes experience in long-duration <u>space flight</u> and a reputation for reliability.

The average working lifespan of a scientist puts a practical limit on the length of a <u>space mission</u>.

It is hard now to remember the alarm in Washington which greeted the Soviet Union's first sputnik in 1957, or the envy aroused by the <u>manned flight</u> of Yuri Gagarin four years later.

NASA and Russian scientists are talking of a joint <u>manned mission</u> to Mars.

In recent years, scientists have identified 'space junk', including a screwdriver dropped by an <u>astronaut</u>, as one of the biggest hazards in space.

Russia showed this week that its <u>cosmonauts</u> can do some things in space that no one else can. On January 9th, Valeri Polyakov began his 366th consecutive day in orbit, passing the record set by Vladimir Titov and Musa Manarov.

161

5 Murder in space, or lack of it. Read the article below from the *New Scientist* and find expressions in it of the number of letters indicated.

1   What is another word for 'stress' used once in the article? (6)

2   Which two two-word expressions in the second paragraph refer to the worst results of stress described in the article? (7,9 and 8,8)

3   Different people have different degrees of tolerance to stress: they have different _____ to stress. (16)

4   What word is used to describe the stress of takeoff? (7)

5   If you continuously check someone's mental or physical state, you _____ them. (7)

6   A period of eliminating the effects of stress, for example in sleep, is a period of _____ . (8)

7   Living in a very small space is described as living in conditions of _____ . (11)

Stop the Rocket, I Want to Get Off

The stark reality of life as an astronaut is becoming increasingly evident to psychologists in the run-up to a mission to Mars.

Cosmonaut Valery Ryumin wrote in his personal diary in 1980: 'All the necessary conditions to commit a murder are met by locking two men in a cabin 18 by 20 feet for two months.' As far as the Western world knows, Soviet space missions never went that far, despite missions lasting more than a year in the 90 cubic metres of the Mir orbital station. ...

In 1985, a six-month mission was cut short when one cosmonaut had a nervous breakdown. He contracted a cold and was unable to do his full workload. This played on his mind, making him feel guilty. His cold worsened, so the others had to take on more of his duties. The vicious circle ended in his complete collapse, and the mission was aborted after two months.

The many missions run on Soyuz and Mir are potentially the best source of data on the psychological effects of long-term space flight - vitally important when contemplating crewed space missions to Mars, which will involve a four-year round trip. ...

But there is more to it than relearning the experiences of Mir cosmonauts. Future space missions will be significantly different. Most astronauts will be civilians - scientists, doctors or engineers rather than military personnel. They will have a greater tendency to question orders and different susceptibilities to stress.

data *17* ⇑

The crews will be bigger (up to eight people, rather than two or four), consisting of different nationalities. The missions will consist of very different phases. In a Mars mission, a frantic takeoff from earth will be followed by a two-year cruise; a busy Mars landing by planet-based experimentation and study. All these factors must be considered both in selecting the astronauts and monitoring them for signs of stress.

During long missions there is a high risk of the different effects of strain accumulating. 'Astronauts have very little recovery time, they work very long hours, but even when they have finished their work, they are not able to withdraw from the work environment. They are also exposed to permanent stresses such as noise and physical confinement. They have to live in very difficult hygienic conditions and they also perceive a constant threat to life.'

Shuttles and stations

space shuttle

space station

weightlessness
zero gravity

dock

A **space shuttle** is a reusable vehicle which is launched into space vertically with the aid of rocket boosters and lands horizontally like a plane. It is used to launch satellites and carry out experiments during orbit around the earth.

A **space station** is a spacecraft in orbit around the earth used for experiment and observation, for example of the long-term effects on the body of staying for long periods in space in conditions of **weightlessness** or **zero gravity**.

When two spacecraft join, perhaps so that crews can pass from one to the other, as crews from the American space shuttle and Russian space station have done, they **dock**.

After more than a month's delay, the space shuttle 'Endeavour' blasted off with five astronauts on board. The crew plan to release and then retrieve two satellites: an $8 million spacecraft to study the Sun and a $25 million spacecraft to 'grow' thin film for semi-conductors.

The Atlantis space shuttle docked with the Mir space station after less than an hour of manoeuvring, and the crews posed for pictures on board Mir about 245 miles above the Earth.

The astronauts have to communicate and work together while they cope with the disorienting effect of zero gravity, and the problem of moving and stopping in zero friction.

The crew members, all ten of them, will work together on various investigations, including studies of the Mir crew's adaptation to weightlessness. 'It's going to be really fascinating for me to get there and see the inside of this vehicle that's been in orbit for nine years,' says Gibson.

6 Replacing the shuttle. Put the sections of this article from *The Economist* into the correct order. (The first section is a and the last is f.)

— There and Back Again —

a As an experimental vehicle, the American space shuttle could have been a triumph. But, at a time of tight NASA budgets, it was sold, not as one approach to one problem, but the answer to everyone's dreams. It would be reusable, fly frequently, and thus cut costs to orbit; it would also take people into space, and give them a place to work when they got there.

b And since the Challenger exploded, the shuttle has no longer been on offer as a commercial launcher. (The Russian shuttle, seen by many as the country's greatest mistake in spaceflight, has yet to fly with a crew.)

c In fact, the shuttle has flown infrequently, and its costs are huge mainly because of the standing army of technicians it needs for its few flights. A rough estimate is $500 million a flight (though when the air force uses it, NASA charges only $115 million).

d It will not take a payload into orbit; it will just prove that an aeroplane can get there. That is a step in the right direction: calling an experiment an experiment shows an endearing honesty.

e The most ambitious of the programmes designed to supersede the shuttle is the X–30, which is currently being designed.

f The X–30 will burn hydrogen fuel with oxygen from the atmosphere in a fearsomely advanced jet engine that can get gases moving faster than the speed of sound. It has to be built out of materials that have never ventured out of laboratories before. It has to fly at 25 times the speed of sound. ...

gas *132* ⇑

Probes

unmanned flight
unmanned mission

probe
space probe

flyby

An **unmanned flight** or **unmanned mission** going beyond the earth's orbit is a **probe** or **space probe**.

A probe passing near an object in space makes a **flyby** of that object.

◆ **LANGUAGE NOTE**
Flyby is also spelled with a hyphen.

Germany is moving away from large-scale manned space projects towards <u>unmanned flight</u>.

Even scientists who strongly advocate the manned exploration of Mars admit that, for the same amount of money, <u>unmanned missions</u> could probably find out as much, if not more.

It took Voyager 2 a dozen years to get to Neptune. A similar craft launched now would take even longer to reach Pluto. However, a smaller <u>probe</u> could get there quicker.

If you intend to send a <u>space probe</u> to Saturn, it's as well to know in advance what you want it to find out for you.

"THAT'S SCIENCE. WE SEND PROBES TO MARS — MARS SENDS PROBES TO EARTH."

On 3 March 1959, Pioneer 4 became the first US probe to escape from the Earth and make a <u>flyby</u> of the Moon before, as expected, running out of power.

7 Frying fate. Read the report below from *The Times* and complete the sentences.

1 What happens to something in the end is its f _ _ _ .

2 When the end of something is unfortunate, this is its d _ _ _ .

3 Two adjectives describe extreme conditions: i _ _ _ _ _ _ _ and i _ _ _ _ _ _ _ .

4 An action which will harm or destroy the person or thing doing it is k _ _ _ _ _ _ _ .

5 If something f _ _ _ _ _ _ o _ _ , it ends weakly after a strong beginning.

6 Things relating to the planet Jupiter are J _ _ _ _ _ _ .

7 If something like a spacecraft is crushed, it c _ _ _ _ _ _ _ .

Probe Races to Stormy Demise

A spectacular fate awaits a tiny space probe tonight, when it parachutes into Jupiter's atmosphere. The probe, which separated from the unmanned Galileo spacecraft in July, will beam back to Earth 75 minutes of information about the Jovian atmosphere, before either frying in the intense heat, or crumpling under the immense atmospheric pressure.

Scientists will not know for nearly an hour whether the kamikaze probe, which enters the Jovian atmosphere at 10.56pm London time at more than 100,000 miles an hour, has successfully penetrated the planet's clouds of ammonia.

If it does, it will drift down through a layer of ice crystals and water droplets, making the first direct observations of Jovian temperatures, pressures, winds and electric currents. The radio link will then fizzle out, a prelude to the death of the probe.

Galileo will not undergo the same doom as its daughter probe when it also reaches Jupiter, 484 million miles from Earth. Just after 1am tomorrow, the spacecraft will brake, fire its engines and go into orbit around the planet for two years. It will send back information about the turbulent weather in the largest planet in the solar system. ...

crystal *135* ⇑

The sun and the planets

sun
solar
  solar mass
  solar system

planet
  inner planet
  jovian planet
  outer planet
  terrestrial planet

planetary
  planetary system

interplanetary

extraterrestrial
terrestrial

A **solar system** contains **planets** and other objects that orbit a central **sun**. The adjective relating to 'sun' is **solar**. Objects in space are sometimes compared in size to our sun and measured in **solar masses**, the sun being equivalent to one solar mass.

The planets closest to our sun are the **inner planets** or **terrestrial planets**. Those further away are the **outer planets** or **jovian planets**.

The adjective relating to 'planet' is **planetary**. Any system of planets revolving around a star is a **planetary system**. **Interplanetary** is used to refer to things such as space or travel between the planets.

The adjective relating to Earth is **terrestrial**. Things not from Earth are **extraterrestrial**.

◆ **LANGUAGE NOTE**

Alternative spellings for **sun** and **solar system** are **Sun** and **Solar System**, especially when referring to our own.
An alternative spelling for **jovian** is **Jovian**.
Extraterrestrial is also spelled with a hyphen.

Mercury is the most inhospitable of planets in the Solar System. The Sun blazes down on its barren landscape, raising the temperature to 430 degrees C, twice as hot as a typical domestic cooker.

The minimum possible mass of HDE 226868 is 16 solar masses, implying that its companion has a mass seven times that of the Sun.

mass 137 ⇑

The probes would continuously return information about the nature of the interplanetary environment near the earth and quantify the influence of the solar wind, the stream of protons, electrons and helium nuclei constantly emitted from the Sun.

proton 140 ⇑
electron 140 ⇑
nucleus 140 ⇑

Being able to compare the internal structure of Mercury, Venus, Earth and Mars (the four inner planets) is crucial to our understanding of how the Solar System formed and the subsequent evolution of the planets.

Pluto and most moons of the outer planets consist of rock and water ice in varying amounts.

The Solar System has equal numbers of terrestrial and jovian planets, and this pattern is likely to be typical of other planetary systems too.

The hope of finding life elsewhere has helped drive planetary science.

Perhaps Martian microbes differ sufficiently in their biochemistry from <u>terrestrial</u> life that the Viking probes could not detect their presence.

microbe **89** ⇑

This year marks the 35th anniversary of the first Search for <u>Extraterrestrial</u> Intelligence (SETI) experiment.

lunar
moon
satellite

Some of the planets in our solar system have one or more **moons** in orbit around them. The adjective relating to 'moon' is **lunar**.

Moons are **satellites** of their planets. (Compare this with orbiting spacecraft that are satellites of the earth.)

◆ **LANGUAGE NOTE**
The Earth's **moon** is often spelled **Moon**.

Voyager 1 provided our first views of the outer planets and their <u>moons</u> in 1979, when it passed Jupiter's four large <u>satellites</u>. Before the images arrived on Earth, most people expected these moons to be dead places, looking like our own Moon with its innumerable craters.

The US space probe Clementine spent two months photographing the <u>lunar</u> surface at the relatively cheap price of $80 million. By contrast, the Apollo programme would have cost more than $100 billion at today's prices.

8 Solar system similarities. Read this article from the *New Scientist* and answer the questions.

Where Planets Boldly Grow

Do stars other than the Sun have planetary systems?

...Our solar system divides into two groups of planets. The terrestrial planets, Mercury, Venus, Earth and Mars, are small rocky bodies of low mass with limited atmospheres and negligible number of satellites. The jovian group, Jupiter, Saturn, Uranus and Neptune, in contrast, are gas giants with large rocky cores and huge hydrogen and helium atmospheres. They have rings and many satellites.

Pluto may not be a true planet, but an escaped satellite: with a mass only a quarter of that of our moon, it is much more like a satellite than a planet.

The Solar System has equal numbers of terrestrial and jovian planets, and this pattern is likely to be typical of other planetary systems too. Where might we find other planetary systems?

We can begin by ruling out those kinds of stars that are not likely to have planets. The Sun is a single star. Near the Sun about half of all stars are also single; the rest belong to groups of two or more. The complicated gravitational fields around these multiple stars make it unlikely that they have planetary systems.

The Sun belongs to the second generation of stars to be produced since the Universe began. These contain elements with atomic weights greater than those of hydrogen and helium.

Other more widely spread stars that formed closer to the dawn of the Universe began life with only the two lightest elements. These old stars would not have been accompanied by the clouds of dust - made of silicon, oxygen and carbon - that are probably needed to trigger the formation of planets. Dust is certainly needed to form planets like the Earth. ...

1 Do the terrestrial planets have many moons?

gas 132 ⇑

2 A planet's core is under its s _ _ _ _ _ e .

3 What might Pluto have escaped from?

4 Which planet are the jovian planets named after?

5 If you rule something out, do you exclude it?

gravitation 148 ⇑

6 It is i m p r _ _ _ _ _ _ that these stars have planets.

atomic weight 140 ⇑

7 Which are the two lightest *element 131* ⇑ elements?

8 If something triggers an event, does it cause the event?

Comets, asteroids, and meteorites

comet
asteroid
asteroid belt
meteorite
meteoroid
meteor
meteor shower
shooting star

Comets are small objects made of ice and dust that orbit the sun, often in an elliptical orbit: the diameter of their orbit is much greater in one direction than the other.

Asteroids are smaller, rocky objects orbiting the sun, many of them in the **asteroid belt** between Mars and Jupiter.

Still smaller objects travelling through space are **meteoroids**. Meteoroids passing through the atmosphere and reaching the earth's surface are **meteorites**.

Meteoroids produce streaks of light as they enter the earth's atmosphere: meteoroids visible in this way may be referred to as **meteors**. Many doing so at the same time form a **meteor shower**. Meteors are informally referred to as **shooting stars**.

Comets look much larger than they are because they release gas and dust, but their nuclei are typically only a few kilometres across. Comet Halley is large at 16 kilometres.
gas *132* ⇑
nucleus *140* ⇑

Countless millions of asteroids hug an orbit between Mars and Jupiter, forming a belt that normally poses no harm to life on earth. Occasionally, however, lone asteroids are jostled out of the belt, some to assume earth-crossing orbits. Some 150 asteroids with a diameter of at least one kilometre have been detected so far, with two or three new ones discovered every month.
discover *28* ⇑

The conventional view is that the asteroid belt never contained any objects larger than the present asteroids.

When a big meteorite hits a planet, it launches little meteorites back into space. Meteorites thrown back from Mars hit the earth quite often.

This is the first radar system designed to produce detailed orbit information about individual meteoroids down to a size of 100 micrometres.

Last time the Comet Tempel-Tuttle passed Earth, meteors rained down at the rate of 150,000 each hour.

The annual Leonids meteor shower in November could become a deluge. While this might provide a spectacular display of shooting stars, it could spell disaster for satellites and space shuttle crews.

9 Identifying objects. Match the two parts of these extracts.

1 Far from the Sun, in the cold and the dark, a comet is thought to be just a mountain-sized ball of various frozen gases, some dust, and maybe some rock.

2 A mysterious object that exploded high above the Tunguska river in Siberia in 1908 was a stony asteroid 30 metres in diameter, and not, as many thought, a comet.

3 Since rocks of different composition absorb and reflect light differently, astronomers can usefully classify the asteroids into 16 groups on the basis (more or less) of their colours. Meteorites fall into similar groups.

4 The next meteor spectacle will be the Perseids shower. This has been an annual phenomenon recorded since AD 36.

5 Raup concludes that throughout the history of cellular life, some 60 per cent of all species extinctions may have been caused by the impacts of asteroids, comets, or other extraterrestrial bodies.

species 45 ⇑
extinct 45 ⇑

6 Until now, most scientists believed that the molecules from which the first living things formed were made almost entirely in the Earth's atmosphere. But these bodies either burn up while falling to Earth or hit the ground with so much energy that any organic molecules would be destroyed.

molecule 131 ⇑

a For example, Vesta, the fourth-largest asteroid, reflects light in a unique way: some 50 meteorites match it closely.

b Only when it comes close to the warmth of the Sun do clouds of dust and gas boil off its surface to create an enveloping coat thousands of kilometres across, and a tail millions of miles long.

c If it is true that throughout Earth history, 60 per cent of all species have gone extinct through asteroid impact, then the odds are better than even that homo sapiens will go the same way.

d Now the scientists from Cornell have suggested a new source of organic material – the continuous 'drizzle' of very small dust particles that reach Earth from space.

e The force of the explosion felled trees over an area of about 2,200 square kilometres. It was by far the largest impact in recorded history.

f But the most spectacular show is likely on 22 December, when the Ursids meteor shower is expected to occur. Meteor showers are regular phenomena, and around 11 occur every year.

Telescopes and celestial bodies

telescope

observatory

celestial
   celestial body
   celestial object

heavenly body

Astronomers observe things in space with **telescopes**, often based in **observatories**.

Phenomena in space may be described as **celestial**.

Natural objects in space are **celestial objects**, **celestial bodies**, or **heavenly bodies**.

The four mirrors for the European Southern Observatory's Very Large Telescope (or VLT: astronomers save their poetry for naming celestial objects) are single pieces of glass 8.2 metres across but less than 8 centimetres thick.

There are several suggestions as to what celestial event the Star of Bethlehem might have represented.

Isaac Newton discovered that the same force of gravity that holds us down on earth governs the motions of the celestial bodies.

force 129 ⇑
gravity 148 ⇑

Egyptian pyramids are aligned according to the location of heavenly bodies, and people believed that they had to build to exact mathematical prescriptions in order to ensure the wellbeing of the dead in the afterlife.

10 **Telescope types.** Match the two parts of these extracts.

1   While astronomers and the media fretted and fussed about the health of the Hubble Space Telescope,

2   The reconnaisance telescopes under discussion are essentially small orbiting telescopes

3   The giant telescope will eventually be linked electronically to smaller radio telescopes in orbit around Earth to create

4   Enough light gets through space for us to see thousands of stars with the naked eye,

5   American astronomers are working on a special new type of ground-based telescope

6   If we want to observe the distant galaxies, then we have to use not optical, but infra-red telescopes.

a   which could out-perform the Hubble Space Telescope at a fraction of the cost.

b   and millions with an optical telescope.

c   Why bother to look at the most distant galaxies? Because the further we look out into space, the further we look back in time.

d   a network of radio telescopes with an even wider collecting area.

e   aimed at the earth, attached to a video camera that transmits images back to a ground station.

f   another space observatory was launched almost unnoticed and is returning superb images of the sky.

Astronomical distances

astronomical unit AU	Distances in space are often measured in **light years**. A light year is the distance light travels in one year.
light year	Distances within the solar system may be measured in **astronomical units**. An astronomical unit or **AU** is the average distance between the earth and the sun. There are 63,240 AUs in a light year.
parsec	Distances beyond the solar system are given by astronomers in **parsecs**. A parsec is about 3.25 light years.
megaparsec	A **megaparsec** is one million parsecs.

In 1955, the book recorded the remotest known heavenly body as being 1 billion light years away. Now the record is 3.2 billion.

Pluto's average distance is 39 astronomical units, though it follows a distinctly oval orbit and is presently closer to the Sun than Neptune is.

Mayor and Queloz, who work at the Geneva Observatory in Switzerland, recently presented evidence to a conference of the existence of a large planet around a star in the constellation of Pegasus, about 13.7 parsecs (45 light years) from the earth.

evidence 17 ⇑
conference 26 ⇑

It is difficult to find galaxies that act as reliable indicators of distance beyond 300 megaparsecs.

11 Macho exercise. Read this article from *The Economist* and find:

1   the names of four units: a unit used to measure distances in space, a unit used to measure the mass of bodies in space, a unit used to measure data in computing, and a new unit used to measure astronomical data

2   a word meaning a very great quantity of something

3   a word normally applied to a great quantity of bees

4   a word normally referring to a method of catching fish

5   a two-word expression referring to matter in space that does not emit light

6   a hyphenated three-word expression referring to objects that do not emit light

★★★ Trawling the Heavens ★★★

Astronomers used to look at the sky's signs and wonders one by one. Now they can gather data by the bushel.

Students of astronomy quickly get used to megaparsecs, solar masses and the other odd units with which science measures the cosmos. Now they have a new unit to add to the list: the macho. Roughly speaking, a macho is a gigabyte of data gathered overnight. It is a way of measuring a new sort of astronomy, one which makes use of electronic sensors and computers to look at many different objects at once, thus gathering data in huge quantities.

data 17 ⇑

As a result, some fields of astronomy will accumulate tens or hundreds of times more data in the next few years than they have seen in their entire history. This profusion not only answers more questions; it answers different sorts of questions. In doing so, it may solve some of the most profound questions facing cosmology.

Consider the MACHO collaboration after which the new unit was named, playfully, by Bohdan Paczynski, an astrophysicist at Princeton University. The MACHO team takes its name from the massive compact halo objects it seeks to study. At almost every scale, from that of the Milky Way galaxy that contains the earth, to that of the universe itself, the objects that astronomers study behave as though they are heavier than they really are.

Theorists think the difference is due to various possible forms of 'dark matter'. Massive compact halo objects are one such form, a swarm of sort-of-planets that might fatten up the galaxy. ...

Stars

star
astral
stellar
interstellar
constellation
nebula
magnitude

The Sun is a **star**, a body generating energy by nuclear reactions in the gases in its interior. The adjectives relating to 'star' are **stellar** and, less frequently, **astral**. Space, objects, and movement between stars are often described as **interstellar**.

energy *139* ⇑
nuclear *144* ⇑
gas *132* ⇑

Stars in the night sky are traditionally divided into named groups or patterns: **constellations**.

A star's brightness is its **magnitude**.

A cloud of gas and dust in space is a **nebula**.

◆ **LANGUAGE NOTE**
The plural form of **nebula** is **nebulae**.

An understanding of star formation, stellar structure and stellar evolution is central to the study of astronomy.

"WE'RE PICKING UP THE BIRTH OF A STAR, AND THE DEATH OF A STAR. THE ONLY PROBLEM IS, IT SEEMS TO BE THE SAME STAR."

From ancient times, Chinese astronomers divided the night sky into several hundred constellations, most of which would not be familiar to us. The western system of astral mapping did not become widespread in China until this century. Only a few well-known formations are common to both schemes.

One of the consequences of rapid interstellar travel would be that one could also travel back in time.

Most new stars form with hundreds of others in large complexes of gas and dust like the Orion Nebula. But Beta Pictoris is on its own, 53 light years from the Sun.

The dying star appeared extremely faint - at magnitude 22.7, it was 5 million times fainter than the dimmest stars visible to the unaided eye. Even with sensitive electronic detectors, astronomers needed an exposure time of 2.5 hours to reveal it.

12 Star classes. Read the extracts and complete the commentaries.

Astronomers are increasingly aware that most stars in the Universe appear to be organised in pairs known as <u>binary star systems</u>, or in multiple groupings.

Optical astronomers immediately turned their telescopes on HDE 226868 and found from the motion of the star that it is, in fact, a member of a binary system. The blue <u>supergiant</u> is orbiting, once every 5.6 days, around an invisible companion. Now, even the smallest blue supergiant has 12 times the mass of the Sun, and most stars like this have masses 20 or 30 times that of the Sun.

The satellite will spend some time hunting for <u>brown dwarfs</u>, masses of gas smaller than our Sun, which are too cool to burn and which may make up the Universe's 'invisible dark matter'.

The most spectacular pictures are of a red <u>giant star</u> called h Carinae. It is a star in serious trouble, with bright lobes of gas swelling off it, announcing its death throes. Theory says it will soon become a supernova, though 'soon' in this context means in a million years.

All stars are thought to evolve from burning hydrogen and helium, but towards the end of their life red giant stars exhaust this nuclear fuel and the central portion collapses to form a core. This core will eventually become a <u>white dwarf</u>, with a mass similar to the Sun but a radius similar to that of the Earth.

mass 137 ⇑

binary star system	_____ are very large stars many times larger than the sun.
brown dwarf white dwarf	A _____ _____ is a large star in the later stages of its development, with an exhausted core and gas burning in shells around the core.
giant star supergiant	_____ _____ are the dim remains of stars in the final stages of their evolution.
	_____ _____ do not have enough mass to burn in a normal nuclear reaction and therefore do not give off light.
	Two stars revolving round each other are members of a _____ _____ _____ .

Zwicky realised that a <u>supernova</u> was a star that literally blew itself apart. He suggested that supernovae represent the transitions from ordinary stars into <u>neutron stars</u>, which in their final stages consist of closely packed neutrons. Astronomers took 34 years to discover the first neutron stars, in the shape of radio-emitting <u>pulsars</u>.

neutron 140 ⇑

A <u>black hole</u> forms when a very massive object collapses under its own gravity. At a critical distance from the centre, known as the Schwarzschild radius, gravity is so strong that space-time is bent in on itself, cutting off the region inside from the rest of the Universe.

gravity 148 ⇑
space-time 150 ⇑

Quasars are the brightest objects in the Universe. They can emit 100 times as much energy as our entire Galaxy, yet from a region only twice the size of the Solar System. Most astronomers believe that a quasar is a massive black hole at the centre of the galaxy, greedily sucking in stars and gas, which become so hot that they give off massive amounts of energy.

| black hole |
| neutron star |
| pulsar |
| quasar |
| supernova |

A _____ _____ is a collapsed star whose gravity is so great that nothing can escape it, not even light.

A _____ is a huge explosion which brings about the destruction of a star.

_____ _____ formed in supernova explosions and emitting electromagnetic waves are _____ .

A _____ is a very compact, remote object whose nature is uncertain: the word stands for 'quasi-stellar object'.

◆ **LANGUAGE NOTE**
The plural form of **supernova** is **supernovae**.

Galaxies

| galaxy |
| galactic |
| |
| Milky Way |
| |
| disc |

A **galaxy** is a group of stars held together by the mutual attraction of the gravity between their masses. Things relating to galaxies are **galactic**.

The galaxy containing our solar system is the **Milky Way**.

Some galaxies – the Milky Way is one – are in the form of a **disc**, and a star's position in a galaxy is defined in relation to the centre of this disc.

◆ **LANGUAGE NOTE**
Our own galaxy is sometimes spelled **Galaxy** and the adjective for things relating to it **Galactic**.
Disc is spelled **disk** in American English.

Markarian 421 is a giant elliptical galaxy which includes an active galactic nucleus. It is the nearest of a class of active galactic nuclei called the blazars, which are around 300 light years away.

nucleus **140** ⇑

Astronomers in the US have detected thousands of individual stars near the edge of the disc of our own Galaxy. The stars are twice as far from the centre of the Milky Way as the Sun and should tell astronomers about the remote regions of the Galaxy's disc and how they evolved. The Milky Way's disc, which emits most of the Galaxy's light, is roughly 65,000 light years in radius. The Sun orbits in the disc at about 27,000 light years from the Galactic centre, or about 40 per cent of the way from the centre to the edge.

13 **Looking outwards and backwards.** The word 'galaxies' has been omitted six times from this article from *The Times*. Where does it go?

Hubble Discovers a Galaxy of Galaxies

Hundreds of, some dating back to the universe's infancy, have been detected by the Hubble space telescope. Aimed at an empty piece of the sky in the direction of the Plough and programmed to gather light continuously for a period of ten days, it has revealed stars and four billion times dimmer than those that can be seen with the naked eye.

Besides the classical spiral and elliptical, a bewildering array of shapes and colours have been seen. At least 1,500 at various stages of evolution appear in the pictures.

'We are clearly seeing some of the as they were more than ten billion years ago, in the process of formation,' says Dr Robert Williams, director of the Space Telescope Science Institute. 'In archaeological terms, it is equivalent to finding a royal city, but we don't have the dates yet. We don't know if we are seeing the most distant objects or not. The target at which the telescope's deep field camera was pointed was very small - about the size of a grain of sand held at arm's length,' said Dr Williams. To a ground-based telescope, the area is basically an empty piece of sky. ...

Though the area photographed is very small, it is believed to be representative of a typical distribution of in space because, statistically, the universe looks the same in all directions. ...

The cosmos

big bang
steady state

Hubble constant

red shift

One model of the origin of the universe is the **big bang** theory: the hypothesis that the universe began with the explosion of infinitely dense matter several thousand million years ago and that it has been expanding ever since.

model *21* ⇑
hypothesis *18* ⇑
matter *129* ⇑

Another is the **steady state** theory, explained in the example.

One issue in the big bang theory is the rate of expansion of the universe, or the **Hubble constant**.

Measuring the **red shift** of distant objects is a way of determining the speed at which they are moving away from us: there is a tendency for light to move to the red end of the spectrum as the speed of movement away from the observer increases.

◆ **LANGUAGE NOTE**
An alternative spelling for **big bang** is **Big Bang**.
Steady state is also spelled with a hyphen.
Red shift is also spelled **redshift**.

Astronomers need distance indicators to work out how fast the universe is expanding, and from this, how old it is. To describe the rate of expansion of the universe, astronomers use a quantity called a Hubble constant, which is expressed in kilometres per second per megaparsec. Imagine two galaxies, one of them one megaparsec farther away from the Earth than the other. If the Hubble constant was 80, the more distant galaxy would be moving away from us 80 kilometres per second faster than the nearer one. In the same way, the Hubble constant gives the time that has elapsed since the big bang. A rapidly expanding universe would have been able to reach its present size faster than one that had been expanding more slowly.

In the 1920s, Edwin Hubble observed that distant galaxies look redder than nearby ones. The 'red shift' means that galaxies are receding, and the light from them is being stretched out. The farther the galaxy, the redder its light, so the faster it is receding.

…Hoyle's two co-propounders of the steady-state theory of cosmology. In 1948, Hoyle, Bondi and Gold proposed that the Universe had no beginning and would never end; as it expanded, matter was continuously created out of empty space to fill the gaps.

cosmic
  cosmic background
    radiation
cosmological
cosmologist
cosmology
cosmos

The study of the origin, nature, and evolution of the universe is **cosmology**, and people undertaking it are **cosmologists**. The universe is sometimes referred to, especially in this context, as the **cosmos**.

Related adjectives are **cosmological**, and in some contexts, **cosmic**. **Cosmic background radiation** is radiation emitted throughout the universe and thought to have originated with the big bang.

radiation *139* ⇑

Cosmology is painfully short of facts. There are only four good ones: the galaxies are speeding away from us, the Universe is a bit older than the Earth, the background radiation indicates a hot beginning, and the hydrogen to helium mass ratio is what you would expect from a nuclear furnace. Particle physicists, who have recently joined the ranks of modern cosmologists, seem to think that all the really exciting science occurred before the Universe was between 10 and 32 seconds old.

mass **137** ⇑
nuclear **144** ⇑
particle **140** ⇑

If we are alone in the cosmos, then we face an awesome responsibility to preserve the only truly intelligent species of life in existence: ourselves.

species **45** ⇑

To understand the universe when it is very small, we need a cosmological model which incorporates the principles of quantum theory.

quantum theory **137** ⇑

Humanity should accept that science has eliminated the justification for believing in any cosmic purpose, and that survival of purpose is inspired solely by sentiment.

…the discovery of cosmic background radiation. In 1965 two physicists, Penzias and Wilson, checked the prediction of Gamov that the Big-Bang fireball should have cooled to about minus 270 degrees C by this time. They measured the temperature of radiation from outer space and roughly obtained that temperature.

"IT'S ALWAYS THAT WAY—WHENEVER YOU WANT TO GET SOMEPLACE FAST, IT SEEMS AS IF THE UNIVERSE IS RAPIDLY EXPANDING."

14 **All over so soon.** Read this article from the *New Scientist* and answer the questions.

The End of the Universe as We Know It?

The Universe could be more than twice as old as most astronomers believe and be destined to collapse in a 'big crunch' in 79 billion years. This is the implication of a radical new model for the Universe being proposed by an American cosmologist. He says that all the present observations tally with it.

1 Do observations support the new model?

Most astronomers believe that the Universe is only 10 to 15 billion years old and will exist forever. But a major problem for cosmologists is that some stars in our own galaxy appear to be older than this.

Edward Harrison of the University of Massachusetts has explored one possible solution. He makes the standard assumption that the Universe began with the big bang and that its properties are determined by only two numbers: the Hubble constant, which describes the present expansion rate of the Universe; and UC omega, the mass density of the Universe. ...

2 Is a standard assumption the received wisdom?

3 If X determines Y, does it govern Y?

Harrison's values for the Hubble constant and UC omega together set the age of the Universe at 35 billion years. This allows more than enough time to accommodate the oldest stars in our Galaxy, and suggests that our Galaxy was born within about 15 to 20 billion years after the big bang. Hitherto, most astronomers have thought that the Galaxy formed within about a billion years of the big bang. ...

4 Does this theory allow for the age of the oldest galaxies?

Because UC omega exceeds 1 in Harrison's model, it means that the Universe will someday collapse. At the moment, the Universe is expanding, and is 90 per cent as big as it will ever be. The Universe will attain its maximum size 22 billion years from now, when it will be 57 billion years old. At that time, the gravitational pull of all the mass in the Universe will halt its expansion. For the following 57 billion years, the Universe will get smaller and smaller until it compresses itself into a point and annihilates itself. The total time from the big bang to this big crunch will be 114 billion years.

According to this model, our Universe is finite in size and can be viewed as a sphere of space-time. The distance from the Earth to the opposite side of the Universe is 102 billion light years. At the moment, says Harrison, we can observe most of the Universe, because we can detect light from objects as far away as 98 billion light years.

This is not inconsistent with the Universe being 35 billion years old, because these objects emitted their light when they were much closer to us than they are today. The only objects we cannot see are the few that lie between 98 and 102 billion light years away, because their light has not yet had time to reach us.

In contrast, the conventional view is that the Universe is infinite and we can only observe a tiny part of it. But Harrison thinks his model is more attractive. 'The Universe is closed and finite, does not involve meaningless infinities of space and time and is almost entirely observable,' he says. ...

5 If something attains a certain size, it r _ _ _ _ _ s that size.   **gravitation 148** ⇑

6 To annihilate something means to d _ _ _ _ _ y it completely.

7 Which idea here is repeated in the final paragraph?   **space-time 150** ⇑

8 If X is not inconsistent with Y, does it contradict Y?

9 To what two-word expression earlier in the article is 'conventional view' similar in meaning?

Crossword

Across

3 and 9 down. What a rocket does on blast off: it _____ _____ (5,3)

5 Cloud of dust and gas (6)

8 Explosive star destruction (9)

10 Asteroids orbit here (4)

11 Receding galaxies are associated with this phenomenon (3,5)

12 The solar system may not be the only _____ system in the universe (9)

14 Distance between the Earth and the Sun (1,1)

15 Some planets have many, some none: _____s (4)

16 and 4 down. One of a revolving pair (6, 4)

18 Relating to stars (6)

19 Also relating to stars (7)

20 One parsec is about 3.25 light _____ (5)

21 Plural circular motion, or third person of the verb (6)

Down

1 No personnel on this spaceflight (8,7)

2 Neptune is an _____ _____ (5,6)

4 See 16 across

6 Relating to celestial objects, but also enormous (12)

7 Fixed at one point over the earth's surface (13)

9 See 3 across

13 These get launched (8)

17 No need for boosters here (1,1,1,1)

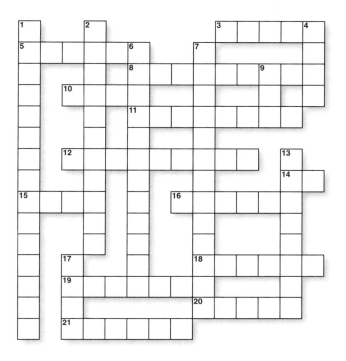

Answer key

1 Research, discovery, and innovation

1 Science partners

1	basic	a	pseudo-
	pure	b	basic
2	applied	c	pure
3	popular	d	popular
4	pseudo-	e	big
5	big	f	dismal
6	dismal	g	applied

2 Science quiz

1h, 2d, 3i, 4a, 5f, 6c, 7g, 8j, 9e, 10b

3 Science divisions

The **natural sciences** are those dealing with the naturally occurring world in general. They include **physical sciences** such as physics and chemistry. **Earth sciences** include geology and oceanography. **Life sciences** include areas such as medicine and biology.

Studies of human behaviour such as economics or sociology are **behavioural sciences**, **human sciences**, or **social sciences**.

4 Technology partners

1 advanced, sophisticated
2 primitive, outdated
3 modern
4 intermediate
5 information
6 digital
7 proven
8 untried
9 wireless
10 manufacturing

5 Inevitable inventions

1 ready, solved; 2 yes; 3 copy; 4 no; 5 yes

6 Blind invention

1 no, 2 spreads, 3 no, 4 no, 5 yes, 6 no,
7 grown, 8 important, 9 no, 10 yes, 11 widespread

7 Technophilia and technophobia

1b, 2d, 3a, 4c, 5e, 6b, 7d, 8f, 9b

8 Researchers and their research

1b, 2d, 3e, 4c, 5a

9 The use of experiments

1d, 2a, 3a, 4a, 5b, 6a, 7a, 8c, 9a

10 Missing link

test tube

11 Disputed parenthood

1 yes, 2 yes, 3 no, 4b, 5 no, 6 no,
7 yes, 8 biology, 9 no, 10 yes

12 Reasoning or intuition?

reasoning: 1, 2, 6; intuition: 3, 4, 5

13 A theory of theories

a, d, e, f, c, b, g

14 Laws and theorems

1c, 2a, 3f, 4e, 5d, 6b, 7g

15 Lines of communication

1 peer, referee; 2 rumour mill, grapevine;
3 disseminated; 4 leaked; 5 gossip;
6 ratified; 7 archive

16 Legendary exploits

1 no, 2 yes, 3 no, 4 all of them, 5 yes, 6 yes,
7 because it has led to a sentimental view of the nursing profession,
8 changes, 9 they sweep clean

Crossword solution

```
                              S
      S  C  I  E  N  T  I  F  I  C        C
         O     X        N        I        O
      I  L     P  H  E  N  O  M  E  N  O  N
      N  L     E        O        N        G
      T  H  E  O  R  Y     V              R
      U     C     I        A  R  T  I  C  L  E
      I     T     M        T        S        S
      T           E        I        T        S
      I  N  V  E  N  T  I  O  N                E
      O           T        N        T  E  S  T  S
      N        L     N     S        U        E
         S  T  A  T  E              B  E  N  C  H
            W     W  H  I  T  E                 H
```

2 The environment

1 Environmental pairs

a campaigners
b benefits
c factors
d impact
e costs
f legislation
g issues

2 Eco-exercise

1	c	i	warriors
2	a	ii	products
3	e	iii	cops
4	f	iv	efficiency
5	d	v	city
6	b	vi	audit

3 Disposal exercise

1 disposal
2 dispose
3 landfill
4 incinerator
5 hazardous

4 Forms of pollution

1b, 2c, 3e, 4f, 5a, 6d

5 Paradise contaminated

1 toxic, 2 found, 3 poisoning, 4 yes, 5 yes

6 The wrong reaction

1 yes, 2 no, 3 explosion, 4 dose, 5 emptied

7 Exploitation, degradation, or devastation?

exploitation

8 Habitat types

1f, 2b, 3e, 4d, 5a, 6c

9 Special species

1 rare
2 endangered, threatened
3 protected
4 indigenous, native
5 alien
6 exotic

10 Worst-case scenario

a, e, f, b, d, c, g

11 Forms of greenery

1 lobby, movement
2 politics
3 issues
4 technologies
5 revolution
6 credentials

12 Sustainable development?

1 no, 2 no, 3 no, 4 yes, 5 no, 6 urgent

Crossword solution

3 Information technology

1 Computer-aided exercise

1c, 2f, 3g, 4e, 5d, 6b, 7a

2 Still useful

1b, 2 no, 3a, 4 no, 5 no, 6 no, 7 no

3 Bit logic

1d, 2b, 3e, 4f, 5a, 6c

4 The advantages of RISC

RISC Business

Although RISC machines have to use many instructions to perform tasks that their rivals could manage with one, they compensate by executing simple instructions very quickly. Several steps are required to perform an instruction in a microprocessor.

First an instruction code is fetched from the memory. Then the microprocessor deciphers this sequence of 0s and 1s to determine what it is being told to do. Then the results of the operation are stored.

To maintain order within the computer, these operations are performed in strict sequence, synchronised to the ticking of a central clock. Simpler instructions allow the clock to tick faster.

But the biggest gains come from taking advantage of simplicity to reorganise the flow of work through the chip.

5 Flash versus disk

	2.5 inch drive	Flash
Capacity	120 megabytes	20 megabytes
Access time	20 milliseconds	250 nanoseconds
Power consumption during access	3 watts	250 milliwatts
Power consumption on standby	500 milliwatts	5 milliwatts
Weight	150 grams	28 grams
Resistance to shocks	5G	50G
Volatile?	not mentioned	no
Reprogrammable bit by bit?	yes	no

6 Keyboard quirks

****** **Qwerty Continuity** ******

...The standard keyboard that was invented in 1872 is known worldwide as QWERTY after the first six letters of the top line of letter keys. The American naturalist Stephen Jay Gould relates that the characters on the QWERTY keyboard were deliberately set to be inconvenient, thus ensuring slower typing speeds.

The reason was simple. Typists using the earliest mechanical typewriters could reach such high speeds that the keys were frequently jamming.

Subsequently, as Gould puts it, by some strange 'technological continuity law', the QWERTY keyboard survived into the age of electronic keyboards, despite the fact that the jamming problem was no longer relevant.

All recent attempts to create a mass market for more efficient keyboards, for example the Dvorak keyboard, on which typists can achieve touch typing speeds about 40 per cent faster than on QWERTY keyboards, were blocked. ...

7 Programmed responses

1 programmed, 2 algorithm,
3 object–oriented, 4 programmer,
5 file, 6 language

8 Counting the cost of programming

1d, 2d, 3a, 4a, 5d, 6c, 7d,
8d, 9d, 10b, 11d, 12c, 13a

9 Matching viruses

1c, 2d, 3a, 4b

10 The next revolution?

1 client, 2 no, 3a, 4 no, 5 no,
6 gamble, 7b, 8b, 9 language

11 Web words

1 home page, 2 browser, 3 web pages,
4 web site, 5 service provider,
6 hypertext, 7 hyperlinks

12 Superhighway logic

multimedia

13 Virtual possibilities

1 applications, 2 games, 3 environment,
4 headset, 5 images, 6 programs

14 Educating Cyc

1 yes, 2 yes, 3 no, 4 no, 5 encountered, 6 no

Crossword solution

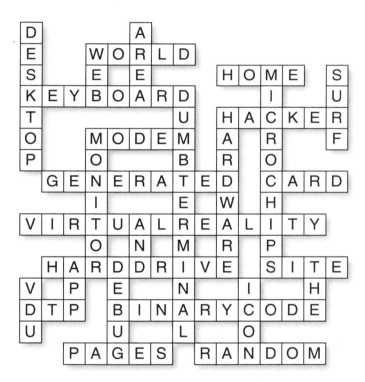

4 Medicine

1 Medical partners

1 care, practice, treatment
2 malpractice, negligence
3 practitioners, profession
4 opinion
5 advances
6 ethics

2 Illness and recovery

If you **contract** a disease, you get it. If you **recover** from an illness, you get better again: you make a **recovery**.

Someone with an illness is **ill**, **sick**, or less frequently, **ailing**.

Parts of the body that are not functioning normally are **diseased**. It is not usual to say that someone is diseased.

3 Self-inflicted injuries

Teething Problems of a Punch-up

Punching someone in the mouth may do more harm to the thrower of the punch than to the recipient, according to doctors who commonly have to treat such <u>injuries</u> in Australia. Over a period of 20 months, Bruce Hall of the Cairns Base hospital in Queensland treated 102 patients whose hands had been <u>injured</u> on the teeth of a victim. The <u>injuries</u> were so severe that many required operations and prolonged stays in hospital.

The patients' ages ranged fom 13 to 49, and all but two of them were men. Ninety of them required operations and the average stay in hospital was more than six days.

Hall says that impact with the teeth of the victim often damaged joints and surrounding soft tissue. Two patients actually had teeth embedded in their <u>wounds</u>. In seven cases, a hand had to be amputated, and skin grafts were necessary in four cases.

Hall says the patients often waited too long before they sought treatment. These <u>injuries</u> represent a considerable cost to the community, he says.

4 Not just psychological

1 elusive; 2 trial and error; 3 fatigue, exhaustion;
4 catch-all; 5 home in; 6 plethora

5 Treatment logic

medication

6 Drug types

1	over the counter/OTC	a	OTC
2	prescription		prescription
3	psychotropic	b	smart
4	synthetic	c	anaesthetic
5	smart	d	synthetic
6	anaesthetic	e	psychotropic

7 Bacteriological logic

1c, 2d, 3f, 4e, 5g, 6b, 7a

8 Death by sandwich

1c, 2d, 3a, 4b, 5a, 6c, 7c, 8a

9 The plague is not coming

1 no, formal; 2 no; 3 noticeable;
4 no; 5 rodent; 6 no

10 To be consumed in moderation

a, c, b, e, d, f

11 HIV at work

1 attacked, 2 ubiquity, 3 no,
4 no, 5 no, 6a, 7 yes, 8 no

12 Surgical combinations

1b, 2c, 3d, 4a, 5f, 6e

13 Involuntary donors

1, 5, 6, and 8 are true

14 Carcinogenic risks

1f, 2a, 3b, 4e, 5d, 6c

15 Catalogue of alternatives

1e, 2c, 3b, 4a, 5d

Crossword solution

5 Genetics

1 Genetic logic

1	make-up	a	testing
2	disease	b	disease
3	predisposition	c	diversity
4	testing	d	predisposition
5	diversity	e	make-up
6	factors	f	changes
7	changes	g	factors

2 Innate ideas

1d, 2e, 3c, 4a, 5b

3   Genetic arithmetic

1 He says that the comparisons of genetic closeness are made on a scale
which does not have its origin at zero;
2 received wisdom;   3 yes, laudable;
4 numerical misapprehensions

4   The four-letter alphabet

1c,   2c,   3b,   4b,   5a,   6b,   7c,   8a

5   Not such junk

a,   d,   b,   e,   c,   f

6   Recombination and evolution

1 no,   2 because they are unable to give birth directly,
3 no,   4 yes,   5 no,   6 yes,   7 exact,   8 adapted,   9 yes,
10 no,   11 recovered,   12 wiped

7   Getting the message

1 primeval soup: referred to as if it was the first course in a meal,
2 dawn,   3 instruction manual

8   Tracking down the culprit

genetic screening

9   Case studies in gene therapy

1c,   2f,   3b,   4a,   5e,   6d

10 Case studies in genetic engineering

1c,   2a,   3d,   4e,   5f,   6b

11 Patent arrogance?

a,   c,   d,   b,   e

12 Not so sure

1c,   2c,   3b,   4a,   5a,   6b,   7b,   8c,   9c

Crossword solution

```
T R A I T S
    N   E   D I S O R D E R S
  Y H   X       N     O     N
  C E       G   D     M     A
C H A R A C T E R I S T I C
  R I     L   N   V     N   G
  O T     O   O   I N N A T E
  M A     N   M   S     N   N
D O U B L E H E L I X   T   E
  S L     D       O     T
C O D E       T R A N S G E N I C
  M       H                 C
E N G I N E E R I N G       S
```

6 Physics

1 Physics types

1	particle	a	vi
	quantum	b	v
2	theoretical	c	iv
3	experimental	d	iii
4	nuclear	e	vii
5	Newtonian	f	i
6	solid–state	g	ii

2 Atomic logic

molecules (plural noun)

3 Property quiz

1c, 2c, 3c, 4a, 5b, 6b,
7c, 8b, 9b, 10b and c

4 Changes and temperatures

The temperature at which a solid becomes a liquid is its **melting point** and the point at which a liquid becomes a gas is its **boiling point**.

When a gas or liquid becomes a solid, it **solidifies**. When a gas or a solid becomes a liquid, it **liquefies**. When a substance becomes a gas or **vapour**, it **evaporates** or **vaporizes**; if it returns to its previous state, it **condenses**.

5 Some like it cold

a, f, e, c, d, b, g

6 Logic of mechanics

1c, 2b, 3a, 4b, 5c, 6b, 7b, 8a

7 A celebrated equation

Mass is Energy

...A fast particle or spaceship will appear to get distorted in shape as an outside observer watches it speeding along. Under normal conditions, a spaceship just needs to apply more thrust energy to go faster. But if it is already at very high speeds, a curious effect takes over: the velocity can't go much higher than it is already, yet the energy being poured in can't just go away. What happens? The energy poured in ends up augmenting the solid mass of the spaceship itself.

This should sound suspiciously familiar. The mass growth is pretty small at first, just a tiny fraction of the energy poured in - what you get by dividing by c^2, where c^2 is the square of the speed of light. Turn that equation around and you get the more familiar form, that energy equals mass times c^2, or $e=mc^2$. ...

8 Top table

1 eight, 2 places, 3 yes, 4 yes, 5 b

9 Fleeting creations

1 doppelgangers, 2 stuff, 3 mirror-image,
4 commonplace, 5 characteristics,
6 indistinguishable from, 7 annihilated

10 Nuclear combinations

1 fuel, industry, plant, reactor, stations, waste
2 arsenal, disarmament, explosion, proliferation, test, warhead

11 The promise of clean energy

	Fission	Fusion
Works well with light elements	no	yes
Works well with heavy elements	yes	no
Nuclei produced in reaction are dangerous	yes	not mentioned
Reaction is easy to start	yes	no
Reaction is easy to stop	no	not mentioned
Fuel is easily obtainable	no	yes
Produces radioactive waste	yes	no

12 Theories of everything

1d, 2c, 3b, 4b, 5c, 6a,
7a, 8a, 9c, 10a, 11d

13 Distorted thinking

1 yes, 2 no, 3 yes, 4a, 5 accelerates, 6 route, 7 no

Crossword solution

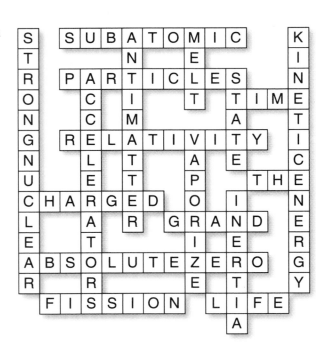

7 Space

1 Space combinations

1	age	a	age
2	agency	b	race
3	programme		agency
4	travel	c	debris
5	exploration	d	travel
6	race	e	Exploration
7	debris	f	programme

2 Powerful propulsion

1a, 2a, 3c, 4a, 5a, 6d, 7a, 8b, 9b

3 Launch pad or launch rig?

1 Baikonur Cosmodrome, 2 no, 3 no,
4 spent rocket stages, 5 no, 6 yes

4 Satellite types

1e, 2 c, 3d, 4f, 5a, 6g, 7b

5 Murder in space, or lack of it

1 strain; 2 nervous breakdown, complete collapse;
3 susceptibilities; 4 frantic; 5 monitor;
6 recovery; 8 confinement

6 Replacing the shuttle

a, c, b, e, d, f

7 Frying fate

1 fate; 2 doom; 3 intense, immense;
4 kamikaze; 5 fizzles out; 6 Jovian; 7 crumples

8 Solar system similarities

1 no, 2 surface, 3 the orbit of another planet,
4 Jupiter, 5 yes, 6 improbable, 7 hydrogen and helium, 8 yes

9   Identifying objects

1b, 2e, 3a, 4f, 5c, 6d

10 Telescope types

1f, 2e, 3d, 4b, 5a, 6c

11 Macho exercise

1 megaparsec, solar mass, gigabyte, macho;
2 profusion; 3 swarm; 4 trawl; 5 dark matter;
6 sort-of-planets

12 Star classes

Supergiants are very large stars many times larger than the sun.

A **giant star** is a large star in the later stages of its development, with an exhausted core and gas burning in shells around the core.

White dwarfs are the dim remains of stars in the final stages of their evolution.

Brown dwarfs do not have enough mass to burn in a normal nuclear reaction and therefore do not give off light.

Two stars revolving round each other are members of a **binary star system**.

A **black hole** is a collapsed star whose gravity is so great that nothing can escape it, not even light.

A **supernova** is a huge explosion which brings about the destruction of a star.

Neutron stars formed in supernova explosions and emitting electromagnetic waves are **pulsars**.

A **quasar** is a very compact, remote object whose nature is uncertain: the word stands for 'quasi-stellar object'.

13 Looking outwards and backwards

Hubble Discovers a Galaxy of Galaxies

Hundreds of galaxies, some dating back to the universe's infancy, have been detected by the Hubble space telescope. Aimed at an empty piece of the sky in the direction of the Plough and programmed to gather light continuously for a period of ten days, it has revealed stars and galaxies four billion times dimmer than those that can be seen with the naked eye.

Besides the classical spiral and elliptical galaxies, a bewildering array of shapes and colours have been seen. At least 1,500 galaxies at various stages of evolution appear in the pictures.

'We are clearly seeing some of the galaxies as they were more than ten billion years ago, in the process of formation,' says Dr Robert Williams, director of the Space Telescope Science Institute. 'In archaeological terms, it is equivalent to finding a royal city, but we don't have the dates yet. We don't know if we are seeing the most distant objects or not. The target at which the telescope's deep field camera was pointed was very small - about the size of a grain of sand held at arm's length,' said Dr Williams. To a ground-based telescope, the area is basically an empty piece of sky.

...Though the area photographed is very small, it is believed to be representative of a typical distribution of galaxies in space because, statistically, the universe looks the same in all directions. ...

14 All over so soon

1 yes, 2 yes, 3 yes, 4 yes, 5 reaches,
6 destroy, 7 the Universe is closed and finite,
8 no, 9 standard assumption

Crossword solution

```
U     O           L  I  F  T  S
N  E  B  U  L  A        G              T
M     T     S  U  P  E  R  N  O  V  A
A     B  E  L  T        O     F     R
N     R     R  E  D  S  H  I  F  T
N     P     O           T
E     P  L  A  N  E  T  A  R  Y     P
D     A     O           T        A  U
M  O  O  N     M     B  I  N  A  R  Y
I     E     I        O           L
S     T     C        N           O
S     S     A        A  S  T  R  A  L
I     S  T  E  L  L  A  R           D
O     T           Y  E  A  R  S
N     O  R  B  I  T  S
```

Index of key words

Acknowledgements

The author and publisher are grateful to the following for permission to reproduce the extracts and cartoons on the pages indicated.

Extracts:

Page 7	© *The Economist* London 16.02.91
Page 9	© *The Economist* London 18.06.94
page 10	© *New Scientist* 15.01.94
page 14	© *The Economist* London 14.11.92
page 19	© *New Scientist* 20.02.93
page 23	© *New Scientist* 08.01.94
page 27	© *The Economist* London 16.02.91
page 29	© *New Scientist* 07.03.92
page 36	© *The Economist* London 05.10.91
page 39	© *New Scientist* 12.09.92
page 40	© *The Economist* London 27.04.91
page 48	© *New Scientist* 02.05.92
page 51	© *New Scientist* 09.05.92
page 56	© *The Economist* London 01.04.95
page 59	© *The Economist* London 16.03.91
page 61	© *New Scientist* 21.11.92
page 63	© *New Scientist* 11.02.95
page 67	© *The Economist* London 23.01.93
page 70	© *The Economist* London 14.10.95
page 73	Davey Winder, Contributing Editor Pro
page 78	© *The Economist* London 12.01.91
page 83	© *New Scientist* 20.06.92
page 85	© *New Scientist* 14.05.94
page 92	© Times Newspapers Limited 26.10.95
page 94	© Times Newspapers Limited 23.11.95
page 95	© *New Scientist* 13.02.95
page 96	© *The Economist* London 29.06.96
page 100	© *The Economist* London 21.10.95
page 104	Annabel Ferriman *Independent on Sunday* 24.09.95
page 109	© *The Economist* London 26.12.92
page 110	© *New Scientist* 16.12.95
page 112	© *The Economist* London 25.02.95
page 114	© *New Scientist* 12.08.95
page 116	© *New Scientist* 28.10.95
page 119	© HarperCollins Publishers
page 126	Charles Arthur, Tom Wilkie *The Independent* 20.11.95
page 127	© *New Scientist* 18.04.92
page 136	© *New Scientist* 14.11.92
page 138	© *New Scientist* 25.02.95
page 139	David Bodanis *The Independent* 05.08.96
page 141	© *New Scientist* 12.02.94
page 143	© Times Newspapers Limited 06.01.96
page 146	© *The Economist* London 16.09.95
page 149	© *The Economist* London 05.01.91
page 151	© *New Scientist* 02.01.93
page 156	© *New Scientist* 25.01.92
page 158	© *New Scientist* 13.05.95
page 162	© *New Scientist* 17.04.93
page 164	© *The Economist* London 15.06.91
page 166	© Times Newspapers Limited 07.12.95
page 169	© *New Scientist* 12.12.92
page 174	© *The Economist* London 09.09.95
page 178	© Times Newspapers Limited 17.01.96
page 181	© *New Scientist* 16.01.93

Cartoons:

pages	11, 31, 34, 37, 38, 55, 59, 68, 74, 75, 80, 84, 93, 98, 99, 101, 103, 113, 118, 138, 150, 159, 172 © Kate Charlesworth – these cartoons originally published in *New Scientist*
pages	1, 5, 16, 18, 22, 28, 35, 44, 46, 47, 57, 77, 106, 121, 123, 125, 129, 140, 146, 148, 153, 161, 165, 168, 175, 180 © 1993 by Sidney Harris – *From Personal Ads to Cloning Labs*, New York, WH Freeman
page 13	Joseph Farris, Cartoonists & Writers Syndicate
page 111	© Buddy Hickerson
page 155	Jack Ohman

Every effort has been made to contact owners of copyright material. If there are any omissions, the publisher will be glad to rectify these when the title is reprinted.